21/F

(

D0830675

Play and the Sick Child

Play and the Sick Child

EVA NOBLE

FABER & FABER, 24 Russell Square London

First published in 1967
by Faber and Faber Limited
24 Russell Square London W.C.1
Printed in Great Britain by
Latimer Trend & Co Ltd Plymouth

Contents

Foreword by Hugh Jolly, M.A., M.D., F.R.C.P.,
D.C.H.   *page* 9

Acknowledgements   11

Introduction–*The play needs of the pre-school child*   13

1–The young child in hospital   19
   The implications of hospitalization   19
   Play can help   25

2–Play facilities in children's wards   32
   Survey of provisions made   32
   Detailed observations of the play of children in hospital   34
   Discussion of findings   88
   Assessment of provisions made   102

3–Doll-play projective test   106
   *Reasons for selection, children selected, and structure and
     administration of the test*   106
   Detailed reports of the doll-play   111
   Assessment of findings   152

Conclusions   156

Bibliography   158

Index of Themes   163

Index of Persons mentioned in the text   165

Illustrations

List of figures

I   Time samples showing the play of children in hospital   *pages* 95–98

2   Diagram of layout of 'ward' in doll-play projective test   108

3   Average scores in doll-play projective tests   150

List of plates

i   Domestic play helps to maintain that vital link with home   *facing page* 32

ii   Soap and water are very satisfying   33

iii Dough is clean and satisfying to handle   33

iv   Social contacts are important   48

v   A plentiful supply of toys is not enough   48

vi   A constructive toy can give a sense of security   49

vii Painting is fun   49

viii 'This is the way Mummy does it'   64

ix   Play goes on in spite of a difficult position   65

x   Sand and water promote long periods of settled play   80

xi   Playing out hospital procedures   81

xii Music not only gives pleasure but has great therapeutic value   81

Foreword

Miss Noble's observations on children in hospital are so illuminating and at the same time so frightening in their implications, that anyone reading this book is bound to want to do something to remedy the situation. That a small child could solemnly eat the fur from his teddy bear for the whole of the hour's observation period is horrifying, yet few of us looking after children in hospital could be certain that such an incident would not take place in one of our wards.

Those who care for children in hospital are naturally devoted to them so that none are exposed to unnecessary pain. Why then should it be possible for the appalling disclosures in this book to take place? The answer can only be in ignorance of the place of play in the life of a child in hospital. It is through play that a young child learns to adjust to his environment. If this is necessary at home, how much more is it needed when he is in hospital? But there are still matrons and ward sisters who tell their staff not to waste time playing with the children when they should be working; such individuals must be unaware that playing with a child is work for the adult.

No one reading this book can doubt the need for the provision of adequate play facilities in every children's ward. A plentiful supply of toys is not enough, there must be someone appointed to supervise play. A Play Supervisor does not supplant the mother's or the nurse's care but supplements both. Miss Noble has found that the nursing staff take more interest in the children's play where special provision for play is provided. It is easier to make contact with children who are happily occupied than with those who are bored and apathetic. Moreover, play not only keeps the child happy but gives the skilled observer the opportunity to interpret his needs, thereby reducing much of the emotional trauma resulting from admission to hospital.

There is no limit to the type of play which is suitable for hospital. Miss Noble has shown that it is possible to use water and sand on a child's bed and still keep friends with the ward sister!

The general lack of proper play facilities for children in hospital is appalling. It is a sinister thought that Miss Noble was refused permission to study play in isolation hospitals. All children's wards should employ a Play Supervisor, such a person being regarded as an essential member of the hospital team.

HUGH JOLLY

Acknowledgements

I would like to express my thanks to Miss Cass of the Institute of Education, London University, for her help and advice; to Miss McPherson and colleagues past and present at the Royal National Orthopaedic Hospital School, on whose work much of this study is based; and to all hospitals and schools concerned for their co-operation.

I would also like to thank the Medical Photographic Department of the Institute of Orthopaedics for permission to use their photographs and also Syndication International for two of their photographs.

I wish to thank the Department of Child Development at the Institute of Education, University of London, under whose auspices this study was made.

E.N.

Introduction

Of recent years a good deal of attention has been paid to the effects of maternal separation on young children in hospital, largely as a result of the work of John Bowlby and James Robertson. The Platt Committee Report with its recommendation of unrestricted visiting by parents is slowly being implemented. Both medical and nursing staffs, as well as parents, have become increasingly aware of the psychological needs of hospitalized children, but it would appear that one very important aspect, that of emotional outlet through play, is not being given sufficient attention.

The child at home and in the nursery school demonstrates very clearly his need to express his tensions, frustrations and dissatisfactions in a physical manner through his play materials, very often in an aggressive way. If the child at home behaves in this way under emotional stress, what can he substitute in hospital, where tensions are increased a hundredfold and physical activity is reduced to the minimum? If hospitals are to undertake to care for the whole child, physically, mentally and emotionally, they should surely provide suitable play facilities supervised by an understanding adult, as an integral part of their treatment.

While it is generally recognized that young children in hospital need something to play with, consideration is not always given to the suitability of the toys or to the necessity

13

for trained supervision of play. Experience in a hospital school which does provide such facilities appears to show that purposeful play, with a good adult relationship, can do much towards relieving tension and anxiety and at the same time reveal danger signs of psychological disturbance. A stay in a hospital ward with good play provision can even become a positive and enjoyable experience. This is demonstrated by Sally, who returning four years later to the hospital where she had spent fifteen months at the age of three, had her case packed a week beforehand in eager anticipation and knew exactly which occupation (baking) she was going to ask for when she arrived there.

The aim of this study was to try to evaluate the contribution which skilfully supervised play can make to the psychological well-being of young children in hospital, with a view to emphasizing the need for such play for all children, whether their stay be long or short.

The investigation was carried out in two parts. The first was a survey of provisions made in twenty hospitals in the London area where detailed observations were made of fifty children, aged two to five years. The second was the use of a doll-play projective test, using the hospital situation, with children who had been hospitalized between the ages of two and five years, but who were now attending schools for the physically handicapped. These latter were selected because they were more readily available for testing than children in their own homes. The age-range is that of the normal nursery school.

The play needs of the pre-school child

Towards the end of the nineteenth century Spencer, in *The Principles of Psychology*, suggested that children play because

14

they have a super-abundant supply of energy. Groos, writing on the *Play of Man* in 1901, regarded it as an expression of the instinct that impels young animals to train themselves for maturity, whereas Stanley Hall, in *Aspects of Child Life and Education*, expressed his beliefs that children at play recapitulate the progress of the race. In this century the psychoanalytic theory of play put forward by Freud, Melanie Klein and others, regards it as a symbolic form of ideas and thoughts related to infant sexuality. Whatever may be the fundamental nature of play, modern psychologists and educators are agreed that it has an all-important function in laying the foundations of mental health. It is through play that the young child learns to master his environment, to come to some understanding of himself within that environment, to deal with the strains and stresses of daily living, to adapt himself and his emotions to the demands which society makes upon him and to make satisfactory relations with the people around him. Erikson[1] defines the difference between adult and childish play thus: 'The playing adult steps sidewards into another reality, the playing child advances forward to new stages of mastery.'

For purposes of this discussion a somewhat arbitrary grouping of types of play is used though there is in fact a good deal of overlap.

The play activities of the infant and toddler are largely sensory-motor, an exploration of the nature of his physical world, a 'getting into everything', an exercising of his developing motor skills, a revelling in the experience of movement, sound, taste and smell. Characteristic of this stage are the very rapid shifts in attention and active movement from place to place. This sense-pleasure play, which continues throughout life, grows more complex as the child matures, becoming interwoven with other patterns of play. Even in

[1] Erikson, *Childhood and Society*.

infancy it begins to branch out into skill-play, for the child will repeat an action over and over again, delighting in its acquisition. Functioning for pleasure, what Piaget[1] calls 'functional assimilation', leads to a feeling of power, a feeling comparable to that of an adult with a car.

In the earlier stages of the pre-school period the child is more concerned with the nature of the material itself than with using it as a means to an end. He is exploring the possibilities of paint and clay; he is more concerned with problems of size, balance and ways of combining blocks than he is with building things. At a later stage, however, he will often plan and carry out a picture or make increasingly complicated structures with his blocks, using them as a setting for dramatic play. As he himself becomes better able to shape his raw materials he begins to demand a greater degree of reality in his playthings. To a three-year-old a block can be a train, a plane or a bed, but for the five-year-old it is simply a building material and he will want something more nearly representing a plane or a train, even if it means concocting it himself with wood, hammer and nails. In the process of mastery, the discipline imposed by raw materials leads to self-discipline and mastery of feelings.

At first dramatic play is somewhat disjointed but by the end of the pre-school period some quite elaborate themes may be worked out. While the three-year-old can dress himself up quite happily with a drape of material, the four-year-old needs at least one realistic 'prop' to turn himself into a fireman or a cowboy and the five-year-old is beginning to demand the whole regalia. Interacting with his world is one of the ways in which the child gets to know it, but he can also get to know it by acting it. As he starts to become aware of other people having an existence apart from his own, dramatic play

[1] Piaget, *Play, Dreams and Imitation in Childhood.*

becomes an important part of his development; through this
he learns about the society in which he lives, gaining a sense
of power and accomplishment by identifying himself with
adults. At first the central theme is mostly domestic, playing
mothers and fathers, using the situations most vital and most
familiar to him; later he brings in the outside world, playing
engine driver, fireman, policeman, pilot or doctor.

Even in the most favourable circumstances a child may find
himself confronted by disturbing problems and anxieties giving rise to a frightening intensity of feeling which he must
learn to manage and control. He needs to 'play it out'. This
'playing it out' process may take the form of symbolic repro-
duction of painful occurrences, not so that the pain shall be
preserved but so that it may be rendered bearable and therefore assimilated. Piaget[1] says that 'symbolism provides the
child with the live dynamic individual language indispensable
for the expression of his subjective feelings for which col-
lective language alone is inadequate', and Wall[2] considers that
this assimilative and cathartic function of play is most important from the point of view of constructive and preventive
work for the healthy emotional development of children.
Just as the worried adult is not able to give his mind to his
work, so the child's unresolved inner tensions inhibit his mental alertness and active interest in the world around him, thus
cutting him off from a vital source of learning. Miss Boyce[3]
found that the 'law and happiness' so necessary to learning
came to her school when 'material and freedom did its work
by providing the outlet for so many tangles and so much
repressed energy'.

In *Childhood and After* Susan Isaacs states that human rela-

[1] Piaget, *Play, Dreams and Imitation in Childhood.*
[2] Wall, *Education and Mental Health.*
[3] Boyce, *Play in the Infant's School.*

tionships are first in the list of what children need. Within the framework of a warm human relationship children may safely express themselves, sure of approval of their play, which to them means approval of themselves as persons; they can rely on not being rejected however aggressive they may be. This ability to rely on adult acceptance Wall[1] regards as the cornerstone of later ability to accept themselves, one of the main essentials of mental health. Not only do children need to be able to rely on the acceptance of adults but also on their power to help them control their aggression and channel their destructive tendencies. They need not only the materials and opportunities for developing various bodily skills but wholehearted and consistent recognition of their accomplishments, the feeling that adults take as much pleasure in their successes as they do themselves. They need someone sufficiently skilled to know when to give help and when to withhold it; in the words of Susan Isaacs,[2] 'when to see the baby in the child and when to respond to the man he is to be'.

It is in the pre-school years particularly that the greatest opportunities occur for helping children to develop fully through their play. As Gesell[3] says: 'Never again will the child's mind, character and spirit advance so rapidly as in the formative pre-school period. Never again will he have equal chance to lay the foundations of mental health.'

[1] Wall, *Education and Mental Health.*
[2] Isaacs, *The Educational Value of the Nursery School.*
[3] Gesell, *Mental Growth of the Pre-School Child.*

I – The young child in hospital

The implications of hospitalization for the young child

In trying to evaluate what hospitalization means to the young child it is difficult not to paint a rather gloomy picture of 'psychological unkindness'. It should be most emphatically stated that this is not due to individual staff, who are invariably kind and have the interests of their young patients at heart, but to insufficient awareness of young children's psychological and emotional needs, and to a system which grew out of the fight against disease and infection when the need for asepsis was predominant.

SEPARATION

The first and most important factor in the child's emotional life is what Bowlby[1] terms 'a highly discriminated love relationship' with his mother or mother substitute, almost invariably made by the age of twelve months. The breaking of this relationship is an extremely traumatic experience often resulting in deep psychological disturbance. Psychoanalytic studies and work in child guidance clinics have established a firm belief that a warm continuous relationship with his

[1] Bowlby, 'Separation Anxiety'.

19

mother enables the child to develop his innate emotions of anxiety and guilt in a moderate and organized way. Conversely, in a situation of maternal deprivation these emotions may develop to excess, leading to a state of mental ill-health. Hospitalization, which separates the child from his mother, may bring about this state of maternal deprivation.

The work of Winnicott, Spence, Bowlby and more recently Robertson, have stimulated an increasing awareness of the emotional needs of young children in hospital. Robertson's film, 'A Two Year Old Goes to Hospital' has brought home to the medical and nursing profession in particular, that degree of distress and disturbance that even a child from a secure home may suffer from his stay in hospital. In his book, *Young Children in Hospital*, Robertson outlines the three stages through which the child goes when separated from his mother, namely, Protest, Despair, Denial.

In the first stage the child has a strong conscious need of his mother, and since previous experience has taught him that she will respond to his cries, he cries loudly and angrily. The second stage may well be quieter, so often erroneously thought of as the 'settling in' stage. The child is still very conscious of his need of his mother but a feeling of hopelessness is creeping in, a feeling equated by some writers to that of mourning in adults. This 'quiet' stage has led to much of the controversy about visiting, since, when the mother arrives, the child feels able to give vent to the grief and anger which he had submerged, and she is considered to have upset him. The final stage may come when the child has been in hospital a long time. Unable to tolerate any longer the intensity of his distress, he begins to repress his feelings for the mother who, to his mind, has failed him, and to take what appears to be a lively interest in his surroundings. He is thought to have 'settled in' at last.

20

In an article on visiting children in hospital Moncrieff and Walton[1] say that short-stay cases go through a few days of misery followed by a period of adjustment and then, after going home, a period of disturbance. The amount of trauma suffered by short-stay cases has still not been assessed, but many parents report quite deep-seated disturbance following hospitalization for tonsillectomy. With regard to a longer period of separation Bowlby[2] *et al.*, in an investigation into the effects of mother-child separation, found a strong suggestion that a break of more than six months at a critical stage of the child's social development might result in more or less permanent impairment of the ability to make relationships. In a study[3] of children who had been treated at the Burns Unit of the Birmingham Accident Hospital there was evidence of disturbance in about four-fifths of children with burns; analysis showed that the only cause of any statistical significance was the lack of parental visiting to children under five.

The Platt Committee Report of 1959 recommended unrestricted visiting of parents and the Ministry of Health accepted the Report, making it quite clear that this was now official policy. While this has to some extent been carried out, there is still a wide variation of visiting rules from hospital to hospital, and indeed within individual hospitals.

LOSS OF SECURITY

Feelings of insecurity do not only arise from separation. If the mother herself is insecure in the hospital situation she may well communicate this feeling to her child. In a normal family circle the parents are in complete control and, as far as the

[1] *British Medical Journal*, 5th January 1952.
[2] Bowlby *et al.*, *Effects of Mother-Child Separation*.
[3] J. M. Woodward, 'Parental Visiting of Children with Burns', *British Medical Journal*, 22nd December 1962.

child is concerned, all-powerful; they provide the framework of security within which he can develop fully and happily. In hospital he may see them uncertain and diffident, often afraid even to do the simplest things for his comfort without first asking for permission. Hospitals on the whole have an aura of professional efficiency that is apt to make the layman feel timid and inadequate, as some of the letters from parents, edited by Robertson in *Hospitals and Children*, indicate.

A sudden complete change of environment can be very disturbing to a young child even when made with his parents; being left in a hospital ward in charge of strangers causes a complete upheaval of his whole world. In normal circumstances he might be able to come to terms with his fear of the unfamiliar by exploring it; in hospital he is obliged to live in a strange new world that he cannot fully explore. Unfortunately many hospitals add to the frightening anonymity of this strange new world by substituting hospital clothes for his own (for purely practical reasons) thus removing a valuable link with home. That clothes symbolize home and mother quite strongly for the young child is demonstrated by the attitude of children in Nursery Schools who often refuse to remove their coats or jerseys when they are not yet fully secure there without their mothers. This feeling of insecurity within a strange environment may also be increased by the placing of cots in the centre of the ward where the child has no feeling of the friendly protection of a wall behind him. Change of routine, unsettling even for the young child within his family circle, may mean the severing of yet one more link with home.

Constant changes of staff can be a most damaging factor in the life of the child in hospital, as the Platt Committee Report points out. It is probably only a question of time before all hospitals will have arrangements at least for completely unrestricted visiting if not for 'mothers in', but there will always be some children whose mothers cannot visit daily, or unhappily in some cases, do not wish to visit. Such children suffer badly from the almost universal type of hospital organization which has split duties and which, for reasons of training, changes the nursing staff frequently. The Ward Sister is often the only stable figure in the child's life and she has to divide her attention between far too many children and staff to be able to provide the degree of stability they need. One child in the observations which follow had been in hospital for twenty-three months, rarely visited by her mother. In this hospital the nurses, both day and night staff, are changed every eight weeks, so that this child had had twenty-three complete changes of staff, the Ward Sister and the orderlies being the only constant figures in her life. Some hospitals make an attempt to ameliorate this situation by employing nursery nurses to provide continuity of handling.

The most sympathetic understanding of children's emotional needs cannot prevent that loss of security which comes with painful procedures. This may be greatly reduced by allowing the mother to be present when such procedures are carried out. However, hospital must necessarily come to represent to the child the place where something unpleasant and painful may happen to him at any time. This particular form of insecurity might well be exacerbated by the fundamental fear of losing a part of oneself. Stone and Church[1] state that in the later pre-school period children have very strong feelings about being complete and quote the remark of Stuart, who was to have a tonsillectomy: 'I do not like myself not to be myself and what will happen if even my littlest tonsils is taken away from me.'

[1] Stone and Church, *Childhood and Adolescence.*

The young child in hospital

Curtailment of physical freedom deprives the child in hospital of many sources of pleasure and learning. Charlotte Buhler[1] found that the child in the family situation touches on the average seventy-one different objects in the course of a day. Observations of children at home or in a nursery school show what a large part movement plays in their normal life. Fortunately few hospitals now confine children to bed unless it is absolutely necessary. Children who are confined to bed suffer not only from this physical restriction but also from lack of freedom to make physical contact with adults as the mood takes them. The child encased in plaster is unable to run to his mother and indulge in those many spontaneous embraces he would enjoy in the ordinary way. A characteristic trait of a much hospitalized small child is to cling to the hand of any friendly passer-by, demonstrating that 'touch hunger' found in deprived children by Bettelheim and Sylvester.[2]

TIME

The young child has little conception of time; even up to quite an advanced age children have difficulty in distinguishing between today and tomorrow. Stern[3] quotes a boy of four as saying: 'Is today tomorrow? Is it now today? If we go home then will it be today?' It is this lack of conception of time which makes it impossible to comfort a child by telling him that Mummy will come soon. The two-year-old crying in hospital and reiterating 'Mummy come soon' means 'Mummy come now'. As Melanie Klein[4] says: 'He behaves as

[1] Charlotte Buhler, *From Birth to Maturity*.

[2] American Journal of Orthopsychiatry. 18. 191.

[3] Stern, *Psychology of Early Childhood*.

[4] *Vide* Bowlby, 'Separation Anxiety', Journal Child Psychology & Psychiatry. Vol. i.

if he were never going to see her again.' The young child is at the mercy of the immediate situation; he is quite unable either to draw comfort from memories of the past or to look forward to a future in which his mother will come to him. In Bowlby's[1] words: 'It is this inability to imagine a time of deliverance which together with a sense of helplessness accounts for the overwhelming nature of his anxiety and despair.'

Play can help

'The skilled direction of young children's play can be of special value at a time when they are deprived of a home environment.'[2]

While there is no doubt that Mother's presence comes first in fulfilling the emotional needs of young children in hospital, the skilful provision of play can do much to help them cope with the tensions, anxieties and frustrations which are inevitable in the hospital situation. The adult can usually diminish his emotional pain by telling others what he has suffered but a young child's vocabulary is not sufficiently well developed to allow him to find relief in words; his one medium of self-expression which is self-healing is play.

THE ROLE OF THE PLAY SUPERVISOR

Children are only able to gain the maximum benefit from their play within a framework of security. In a hospital ward where they are required to adapt to so many changes of staff and to the demands of so many different personalities, it is

[1] *Vide* Bowlby, 'Separation Anxiety', Journal Child Psychology & Psychiatry. Vol. I.
[2] Education of Patients in Hospital – Ministry of Education Circular 312, — 7.

important for them to form a stable relationship with one person. Although the Ward Sister is a constant figure, she has to spend so much of her time in administration, supervision, training of staff, and medical treatment, that she is unable to pay as much attention to their play needs as she might wish. A play supervisor, on the other hand, has time to talk to the child and to take his play seriously. She is directly associated with the pleasurable experiences of toys and story-telling. By virtue of her training she understands his play needs both in sickness and in health and can make sure that he has the right kind of material both to entertain him and to help him to work out his difficulties.

Just as it is the aim of the Nursery School to supplement rather than supplant the home, so the Play Supervisor in hospital aims to supplement Mother care. She is able to help the child by talking to him about his mother, by reading his postcards to him, by helping him to make pictures to send or to give to her and by giving him affection and comfort when he is lonely. Because she is a familiar figure connected with the everyday world she can give support to the mother by discussing with her non-medical problems concerning her child. By her very presence she may help to moderate that over-intensity of feeling which often exists between mother and child in this highly emotional situation. The child too may gain additional security in seeing mother and supervisor co-operating in understanding his needs. It is essential that the play supervisor should bear in mind the importance of home and mother in relation to the child, for no matter how expertly he may be dealt with in hospital, home is the dominant factor in his life.

The child in normal circumstances can move freely about his world, selecting the play materials to suit his moods and help him to cope with problems as they arise. The child in a hospital ward is living in a strange and often frightening new world that he cannot fully explore; he needs the help of a skilful and perceptive adult to interpret his needs and to provide him with the playthings which will enable him to work out his problems and gain mastery over his feeling of helplessness in gaining mastery over materials. Constant adaptation and improvisation of methods and materials are necessary if he is to be sufficiently stimulated to avoid becoming apathetic and unadventurous. It is important that suitable materials should be provided as the need arises. Hartley, Frank and Goldenson[1] state that the child needs an educational therapy designed to help him with his difficulties and conflicts while they are still in process in order to prevent fixation and permanent damage. The skilled worker learns to recognize signs of disturbance, takes steps to provide the right kind of material, and, where necessary, joins in the child's play.[2] 'If the adult enters his (fantasy) world it becomes a less frightening place.'

TYPES OF PLAY

Domestic play, inspired by the provision of toy household equipment such as pegs and washing-lines strung across the cot, irons and ironing-boards, cooking-utensils and dough, teasets and doll's-house furniture, helps to maintain a vital link with home. The young child at home spends a good deal of time following his mother around and imitating what she does. If he is encouraged by provision of appropriate material and the attention of an interested adult, he will also act out these domestic themes in hospital, leading on quite naturally to conversation about how his mother does things and what she might be doing now, thus bringing her nearer and possibly staving off that state of denial described by Robertson.

[1] Hartley, Frank & Goldenson, *Understanding Children's Play*.
[2] Clare Britton, *Children Who Cannot Play*, Play & Mental Health No. 5.

The young child in hospital

It is interesting to note that, in long-term hospitals, domestic play is often superseded by hospital play, and 'Doctors and Nurses' takes the place of 'Mothers and Fathers'. Good use can be made of this interest to help children play out traumatic procedures. With used syringes, old stethoscopes and bandages, or with the doctor and nurse sets sold in most toyshops, they can carry out on their dolls procedures which they themselves must endure, or can give an 'injection' to a long-suffering adult. Erikson[1] describes an episode involving a four-year-old boy shortly after undergoing an operation, '. . . the child reduced his tension by playing out the role of the doctor, becoming in his fantasy master of the situation which in reality had made him a helpless victim'. The material used in the doll-play test (p. 108) has proved most valuable in this kind of situation.

The child in hospital is so much on the receiving end of other people's ministrations that it is valuable for him to have something more helpless than himself to care for. Animals such as rabbits, guinea-pigs, tortoises and hamsters can give great pleasure in this way. Growing plants too can stimulate interest.

While accepting that it is natural for the child to feel angry and aggressive in these circumstances, it is important that opportunity and encouragement should be given to turn the resultant destructiveness towards more constructive play. In the observations many children were seen to be 'taking it out of' their dolls or teddy-bears. Provision of beds, bedding, bandages and plaster can lead to reparation which is less likely to leave them with the feelings of guilt that might arise from ill treatment of a favourite toy or one which Mother has specially brought.

[1] Erikson, *Studies in the Interpretation of Play*, Genetic Psychology Monographs 22 (1940).

Some form of primitive material which lends itself to messy play is of great value to children in hospital. This not only provides an excellent antidote to the unnatural state of cleanliness and order in which they are required to live, but it also gives them endless opportunities for experiment and construction, as well as a legitimate means of working through the destructive feelings of anger, resentment and frustration that are inherent in the hospital situation. Such substances as dough, water, sand and paint can be used quite successfully with children in bed if plastic bed-covers and ample containers are used. Experience with young children in a hospital nursery school has shown that water and sand are particularly valuable play materials, for they are soothing and relaxing, and promote comparatively long periods of concentration. In learning to manage and control these materials children learn to manage and control their own feelings, for it is such[1] 'unpatterned raw material upon which the child can easily project his imagery'.

The more conventional constructional toys, jigsaws and fitting-in toys often have more than their face value for the child in hospital. Apart from giving him a sense of achievement in mastering the manual skills involved they can often give him a sense of security, a feeling that here is a familiar piece of his world that he can safely control. It is interesting to note that William in C. hospital, in the observations which follow, received the construction set with delight because he had one like it at home and he began to play with it with an almost feverish intensity, as if playing with it could help him control this strange situation in which he found himself. Often rather insecure children in ordinary nursery schools will choose to do the same jigsaw puzzles over and over again, gaining comfort and confidence from this somewhat stereotyped material.

[1] Wolff, *The Personality of the Pre-School Child.*

It is important that the child should be able to do something constructive with the toy with which he is presented. For example if he is given 'Dinky' cars he should be given a suitable table or board on which to run them. Several of the observations show small boys in bed, unable to do anything with the little cars or engines that their parents had brought apart from aimlessly twisting the wheels or destroying them.

LANGUAGE AND LEARNING

Difficulties of communication may add to the child's feeling of strangeness in hospital. The language of hospital life is very different from that of home and this may have the two-fold effect of confusing him in his new environment while adding to his feeling of being cut off from the old. The play supervisor can do much to help him in this respect by making sure that he learns the names of the things around him and at the same time keeping alive his home vocabulary by means of domestic play materials. This latter is very important if he is to fit happily into his home environment when he returns. Interesting play materials can also lead to conversation with other members of the hospital staff as will be seen in some of the observations which follow.

Nursery rhymes, finger plays and counting games are all part of a familiar background and can be used with small groups or with individual children. Music too not only gives pleasure but has great therapeutic value.

A wealth of learning experience can be missed even in a comparatively short stay in hospital. It is readily accepted that this is so for school-age children and steps are taken to make sure that no serious gaps shall occur in their education, but the gravity of such a gap in learning through play is often overlooked. With regard to children's play development, Lydia

Jackson[1] suggests that the missing of a stage means a 'mixing up' which leads to psychological disturbance. In seeking the solution to this problem the hospital nursery teacher, aware of the play stages through which children normally pass, must use her ingenuity in providing opportunity and materials for the children in her care. She must understand too that anxiety inhibits learning and that it is necessary to give the child help in working through his anxiety feelings in order to help him to learn.

A carefully devised hospital play programme may well prove to be a useful preventive measure against mental ill-health.

[1] Jackson, *Child Treatment and the Therapy of Play.*

2 – Play facilities in children's wards

Survey of provisions made

In an attempt to assess the value of play in meeting the emotional needs of young children in hospitals, a sample survey of children's wards in twenty hospitals in London and the Home Counties was undertaken. Detailed observations of one hour each were made of fifty children between the ages of eighteen months and five years.

As many different types of hospital as possible were visited, permission in most cases being given by the Matron. These included Children's hospitals, Children's Long-stay, Teaching hospitals and General hospitals. (The classifications are according to the *Hospitals Year Book*.) Isolation hospitals are the only type not represented in the survey, due to inability to obtain permission. Most hospitals were very co-operative but unfortunately it was not possible to obtain permission to visit all those in which children doing the Doll-play Projective Test had spent some time, as had been intended.

In some hospitals all the children's wards were visited and in others only those selected by the Matron as suitable for observation. The times at which the observations were made were arranged to suit the convenience of the hospitals con-

32

i. Domestic play helps to maintain that vital link with home

ii. Soap and water are very satisfying

iii. Dough is clean and satisfying to handle

cerned. Information concerning general policy with regard to visiting and play facilities was obtained either from the Administrative staff or the Ward Sisters; no questionnaire was issued. In order to ensure that no special preparations were made the precise object of the visit was not stated, permission being asked merely to observe the play of sick children in hospital.

The following table shows the number of each type of hospital visited and the type of play provision made.

Type of hospital and number visited	*Nursery Teacher*	*Play Leader*	*Nursery Nurse*	*Mothers*	*No provision made*
6 Children's (A–F)	1	0	2	0	4
2 Children's Long-stay (G, H)	2	0	1	0	0
5 Teaching (I–M)	1	1	1	3	0
7 General (N–T)	0	0	1	1	5

To sum up, of the total of twenty hospitals, two had established schools including the nursery group, two had established schools including the nursery group plus nursery nurses, one employed a full-time (9 a.m. to 5 p.m.) play leader, two employed nursery nurses giving only passing attention to play, four relied on mothers of in-patients and nine made no provision at all.

PROVISION FOR SCHOOL-AGE CHILDREN

Three hospitals had an established school not including the

under-fives, seven had teachers for a stated number of hours per day for children over five, four could call on the services of a teacher, when necessary, for children over five. In two of these hospitals the teachers unofficially gave some attention to the under-fives when time permitted.

Detailed observations

Children of normal intelligence in the age-group two to five years were selected. No contact was made with them beforehand as it was thought desirable that they should be as unaware as possible of being observed. The observer seated herself unobtrusively where she could see the children without being directly in their line of vision. Inevitably some children were aware of her, particularly where their occupations were not engrossing, or where there was no adult present to take an interest in them. Although it was very hard not to do so, the observer took no part in the children's play, not even picking things up if they were dropped on the floor. Each hour's observation was marked off into time samples of five minutes, care being taken to note down everything the children did, their contacts with adults and, as far as possible, what they said.

CHILDREN IN WARDS WHERE NO PROVISION WAS MADE

Children's hospital (A)
A medical ward in a children's hospital, typical of the older type, a little gloomy, rather overheated and therefore somewhat oppressive. The ward generally appeared to lack life and light though it should be pointed out that two of the children were quite sick on the day of observation. The children's ages ranged from a few months to twelve years, the tiny babies

being nursed in adjacent cubicles. Visiting is allowed every afternoon.

The 'up' children were allowed to roam freely around the ward, there being no playroom. There were a few rather battered toys in evidence. Each child had his own teddy, or soft toy, on his cot.

There was a teacher provided by the local education authority for the school-age children but no provision was made for the under-fives and no nursery nurses were employed.

Julie, aged two years, one month, had been readmitted for a second time three days previously for further investigation. Her mother lived and worked in the hospital but her visits to Julie were confined to the afternoons. Julie was a pale, solemn, unsmiling child with a tiny querulous voice. At the time of observation she was up and free to roam around the ward.

10.20 a.m. Trotting around ward—approaches orderly with trolley—picks up a doll's leg that is lying on the trolley, puts it in her mouth and trots around thus. Plays with locker door, goes to boy at table doing school-work—throws doll's leg on floor, wanders around, goes to look at another boy in bed who is crying.

10.25 a.m. Climbs on to a chair by the window and stands looking out. Repeatedly says 'I can't get down' in a little querulous voice that no one hears, but does not attempt to raise it. Nurse comes with mid-morning drinks, lifts her down and sits her on a chair by the table, where she quietly and obedi-

10.30 a.m. ently drinks her milk. When her milk is finished she sits quietly on, watching boy do his school work, and then orderly helping boy in bed to

35

Play facilities in children's wards

10.35 a.m.   dress. Gets down from chair and roams around aimlessly. Pushes chairs around—then returns to chair by table. Climbs on chair by window again

10.40 a.m.   repeating mournfully 'Can't get down'. Orderly lifts her down. Asks 'Is Mummy coming?' Staff Nurse tells her 'Yes, in the afternoon', gives her a doll (unclad) to play with. Drops doll and wanders

10.45 a.m.   off to boy who is putting his shoes on. Roams around, climbs on chair by table—stands on it— sits down on it. Gets off chair and goes across to

10.50 a.m.   Nurse tending baby in cot—tentatively touching the baby's hair and then playing with the locker door until Nurse says 'Off you go and play' (with what?!). Goes to talk to boy at table and then

10.55 a.m.   back to Nurse with baby—back to table, climbs on to chair, wriggling and kicking her legs—kicks her shoe off. Climbs out of chair and goes over to Doctor visiting another child. Staff Nurse puts her shoe on and gives her the doll again, which is quickly discarded. Goes over to baby placed on

11.00 a.m.   floor and plays with her toys—wanders around with baby's rattle in her hand experimentally

11.05 a.m.   sounding it against a variety of surfaces. Picks up doll and thrusts it at boy at table. He takes no notice. Stands doll up on the table and talks to it.

11.10 a.m.   Wanders off to play with locker door, then into the sluice and out again, playing with door. Picks up doll and carries it to the sluice but fails to open

11.15 a.m.   door, so wanders round carrying doll. Goes to Staff Nurse saying 'Is Mummy coming back?'. Staff Nurse reassures her and encourages her to go and play—'Go shopping' (again, with what?!). Wanders off—climbs on to chair by table, off

11.20 a.m. again, goes to desk and fiddles with drawer, returns to chair.

Also observed in this ward was *Anthony, aged one year, eleven months*, who sat in a chair for twenty minutes, just holding his shoe in his hand and staring into space until Nurse came and put him to bed, where he hugged his teddy bear and cried himself to sleep after ten minutes. Staff Nurse said that he was very intelligent but seemed to be absolutely lacking in energy, and that he had deteriorated steadily during his stay (two weeks) in hospital.

Children's hospital (D)

A surgical ward in a children's hospital of one hundred beds, a small ward of ten beds and cots with children of all ages up to sixteen years. The ward was bright and cheerful, with a very free atmosphere. Visiting was daily from 2 p.m. to 6.30 p.m. Children over five years had a teacher if they were in hospital for more than three weeks but no provision was made for the under-fives and no nursery nurses were employed. The nursing staff chatted to the children and were obviously much liked, but did not have time to play with them. There were plenty of books and comics around but few other toys in evidence.

Kevin, aged four years, three weeks, had been in this hospital for three weeks for a colostomy, but he was usually in a children's hospital home and he appeared to have many of the attributes of an institution child. His parents were not able to visit more than once a week. He was in a cot and had on it some Dinky cars and a teddy bear. He was playing with a baby's rattle. He was a bright chatty child. He spent some time turning the pages of a book but broke off frequently to call out to other

37

children or to demand the attention of a nurse. Much of his behaviour was of the 'showing off' variety calculated to call attention to himself. He was very much aware of what was going on around him and looked anxious when a laboratory technician came in, calling 'Is it me?' He told the sister several times that his mummy and daddy were coming after dinner. He tucked in heartily when dinner came.

Garry, aged five years, had been in hospital for eighteen days for appendicectomy. His mother visited daily. He was sitting up in bed unsmiling but with very bright eyes. He had a furry animal, some comics and a jigsaw puzzle on his bed-table.

10.55 a.m.   Talking to girl in next bed who is taking a torch to pieces. Biting the sleeve of his pyjama jacket and looking around, but with unseeing faraway

11.00 a.m.   look. Opening locker and taking out an orange— 'I've got an orange', rolling it around his face—on his bed and on his bed-table. Trying to peel and

11.10 a.m.   pummelling orange. Peeling orange and putting

11.15 a.m.   peel on locker. Talking to girl in next bed and sucking orange. Nurse comes and scolds him for eating his orange before dinner. Puts orange away and resorts to chewing his fingers and pyjama sleeve alternately. Bed-table prepared for dinner.

11.20 a.m.   'I want a blue one' (traycloth, he had been given pink!). Puts fingers in his ears calling 'Sandra, I can't hear cars—I made cars stop—I wanted blue' (traycloth). Looking around—frowning and arranging table cover, crumpling it up and straight-

11.25 a.m.   ening it out again. Lying down, until Doctor

11.30 a.m.   enters ward, sitting up, looking—biting fingers, biting traycloth. Straightening traycloth. Kneel-

11.35 a.m.   ing up and measuring orange juice on bottle on

11.40 a.m.
to
12.00 p.m.

locker with his fingers. Putting traycloth in his mouth and chewing and staring into space. Talking to girl in next bed. Experimenting with bed-table in various positions. Dinner put in front of him—reluctant to eat and distressed when urged —rolling food around mouth and needing a great deal of encouragement and admonition to make him eat at all.

Here also was *Sandra, a little girl of twenty months*, in a hip plaster, lying on her back staring into space for the whole hour, with no toys anywhere near her. No one spoke to her during that time. She made no noise at all until presented with her dinner, when she burst into loud sobs.

Children's hospital (E)

A surgical ward in a small children's hospital of fifty-two beds. There were fourteen cots or beds for children of ten years and under, some of the cots being placed in the centre of the ward. A wireless was playing loudly during the time of observation. The children were mainly in bed at the beginning of the observation, many of them lying passively with no toys but the majority had been dressed and allowed up by the end of the hour.

Visiting may be all day from 10 a.m. but most mothers came in the afternoon only. There were three mothers visiting during the observation and here for the first time the observer saw a mother pick up and nurse a child other than her own.

The nursing staff spent a good deal of time comforting crying children but did not play with them. There was an abundance of large toys such as rocking-horses, rocking-chairs and push toys for the ambulant children. The Sister said that she experienced great difficulty in obtaining a teacher when

39

needed for the over-fives and that no provision was made for the under-fives. No nursery nurses were employed.

Douglas, aged five years, had been in two days for appendicectomy. He had painting-books on his bed but no crayons in evidence. He had a large envelope in which the books had arrived and a card in a smaller envelope. He was lying back looking pale and languid.

10.20 a.m. Taking books in and out of envelope—standing card up on his locker and fiddling with it. Tracing

10.25 a.m. letters on envelopes with his finger. Rubbing face. Lying back on pillow. Fiddling with envelope.

10.30 a.m. Picking nose. Sighing and turning over on side with hands behind his head. Smiles and nods at another child's mother who speaks in passing. Picks up envelope again—waving it and fitting it between cot bars. Another boy hands him a soldier

10.35 a.m. which he stands on his locker. Picks up envelope and apathetically waves it. Fiddles with flap of

10.40 a.m. large envelope. Shows another boy his painting-books. Puts books away and slides down in bed still holding envelope. Plays with his toes. Bal-

10.45 a.m. ances envelope on his knee, playing with flap. Gazing around listlessly and fingering feet. Trac-

10.50 a.m. ing letters on envelope with finger. Mother comes

10.55 a.m. in—gives her laconic greeting. Mother sits by him

11.00 a.m. and looks at his books. She picks up Mark, aged two years, who is crying bitterly for his mother and nurses him by Douglas's bed. Douglas says

11.05 a.m. 'Your Mummy's coming back. I saw her come in'. (She had come in when Mark was sleeping.)

11.10 a.m. Talking more brightly to mother now, showing her his painting-books and talking about them.

11.15 a.m. Mother gives him crayons and encourages him to colour. Says 'I don't know how to do it' in rather a whiny voice. Mother helps him and the two work together happily.

Garry, aged three years, six months, had been in for three days. His mother visited daily. His cot was one of three in the centre of the ward. On it he had a large soft toy and a plastic bus.

10.20 a.m. Playing with socks and standing up at the end of his cot. Sits, rolling sock and looking through bars of cot—puts sock in pocket. Stands up at end

10.25 a.m. of cot looking down the ward—rubs face—picks up bus and gently bangs it against the bars of his cot. Throws sock over side as Nurse passes. Waves bus at a mother visiting another child and looks longingly at her—throws bus over and she goes and picks it up and says something to him—which he receives with a pleased smile. Mother returns to her own child and Garry throws bus down on

10.30 a.m. his cot and watches her. Sits down. Stands up. Swings on end of cot—banging the end. Plays with label on cot. Throws label away and picks up bus. Sits watching another child and his mother.

10.35 a.m. Watches Staff Nurse, looking rather serious and

10.40 a.m. forlorn. Picks up bus and stands with it hanging from his hand. Bites finger. Stands on teddy. Walks round cot. Drops bus. Sits, with lost, unhappy look, playing with toes. Looks expectant as another mother walks down the ward but his face

10.45 a.m. falls when she fails to notice him. Stands. Picks up bus—sits and examines it—waves it—stands holding it and looking over cot side—sits nursing bus

41

10.50 a.m. and turning wheels. Nurse takes him out of cot and he wanders round the ward carrying his bus, then runs it on the table. Climbs on chair by table. Rubs eyes. Climbs down and wanders round. Smiles at Orderly who picks him up and talks to

10.55 a.m. him and takes him to see a baby. She puts him down and he wanders round again, disappears and

11.00 a.m. reappears carrying naked doll which he puts in a chair. Tries all the chairs at the table. Shows Ob-

11.05 a.m. server his bus. Sits at table—puts bus on table— wanders off. Pushes rocking-chair experimentally —returns to table and pushes bus along it—pushing away another little boy who tries to touch it. Pushes bus under table. Wanders around carrying

11.10 a.m. bus. Pulls another little boy in a wheelchair. Wanders. Rubs face. Wanders out of door and comes

11.15 a.m. back with a sweet. Goes on wandering around looking lost.

Children's hospital (F)

The medical ward in a children's hospital of 110 beds. The ward, which had twelve cots or beds, was somewhat dark but the ambulant children had free access to the balcony.

Visiting was completely unrestricted though only one mother was there during the observation, nursing her own child who was isolated behind plastic screens because of whooping cough.

There were plenty of toys in evidence and children were allowed to run around freely. There was a teacher for the over-fives but she in fact was also entertaining the under-fives, which she did unofficially when time permitted. No nursery nurses were employed. On the opposite medical ward all the ambulant children had been taken to the park by the nurses.

There were two spastic children in cots in this ward, left very much to themselves, who were said to be unable to do anything, but observation of their hand and arm movements did raise a question in the observer's mind.

There were in fact no detailed observations to make here as all the children, apart from the spastics, were got up shortly after the observer's arrival and each one went out on to the balcony to the teacher who was with the older children, as the following time samples show.

Clifford, aged four years

10.40 a.m. No toys on his cot. Standing at end of cot sucking his thumb.

10.45 a.m. Nurse comes to get him up. Jumps up and down with excitement. Nurse carries him out for bath, Clifford hugging her all the way.

10.55 a.m. Returns to ward dressed. Takes chair outside on balcony to join group round teacher. Runs in and out of ward, eventually settling down by teacher,

11.00 a.m. nestling up to her and listening to a story being read to the older children.

11.05–11.40 a.m. Joins in measuring, singing songs and nursery rhymes and finger plays with teacher and other children.

Deborah, aged five years

10.40–11.00 a.m. Sitting by teacher on balcony listening to a story. .

11.00 a.m. Runs into ward to fetch her doll and returns to her chair by teacher, nursing it and listening.

11.05 a.m. Joins in singing and finger plays.

Play facilities in children's wards

Mary, aged four years

10.40 a.m. Nurse helps her to dress. She takes a chair on to the balcony and sits close to teacher who is reading s story to the older children.

10.45 a.m. Runs in to locker to fetch a card and then out to

11.00 a.m. teacher again and remains close by her.

11.05–11.40 a.m. Joins in singing and finger play.

A toddler of under two also joined this group as soon as she was up and remained there all the time, apart from making one sortie to fetch her doll.

General hospital (N)

This was a large children's unit in a general hospital, there being two main wards with cubicles opening off them and some isolation rooms opening off the corridor. The unit was bright and airy though the atmosphere was somewhat institutional. The 'up' children had a small room opening off the main ward as playroom and dining-room and this was well equipped with toys. There was little evidence of toys provided on the wards apart from the children's own dolls, teddy bears and comics. The children could not reach their lockers. Their ages ranged from sixteen months to eleven years.

Parents were asked to visit in the evenings only, to put the children down to sleep and while not actually forbidden to come at other times, this was not encouraged. In fact only one mother was visiting on the afternoon of observation. Parents were asked not to visit for twenty-four hours after their child was admitted so that he might get to know and trust the nursing staff, accept them instead of his parents and settle down (sic!).

There appeared to be little social contact between staff and children and crying seemed to be largely ignored. One two-year-old in an isolation room, completely cut off from the ward, had no toys at all and her cot was placed in the far corner so that she could not even look out of the window.

Kevin, aged two years, had been in the ward for four days for investigation of his hip. His mother visited each evening. He appeared to be a rather quiet stolid little boy. He made rather tentative advances to anyone going near him.

2.30 p.m.   Has train, bus and teddy bear on cot. Holding and fingering train. Man appears in doorway of ward. Kevin smiles and points. 'Daddy!' Points to bus. Spins wheels of train. Licks finger and rubs train.

2.35 p.m.   Spins wheels of train. Watches child with Mother expressionlessly. Spins wheels. Tries to attract Observer's attention. Picks at train. Spins wheels. Watches Observer. Picks up bus and shows to Observer saying 'bus'. Puts bus and train end to end. Runs train on bed. Watches Sister attending

2.40 p.m.   to another child—appears rather anxious and his hand shakes. Picks up train. Puts train on top of

2.45 p.m.   bus. Sister pulls cot round so that he can see television—does not show any interest. Shows train

2.50 p.m.   to Ward Maid. Watches doorway hopefully holding train. Picking at train and yawning. Takes

2.55 p.m.   notice of television when music is played and roundabout appears. Holding train, yawning and rubbing eyes, putting finger in ear. Shows Nurse

3.00 p.m.   teddy. Given bed-table for tea and immediately springs to life, putting train and bus on table and wheeling them along—absorbed in experiment of wheels on table (first sign of concentration). Pushes bus with train. Puts bus on edge of table— uses table as tunnel for vehicles—overturns table

3.05 p.m.   —tries to right it—puts train and bus on pillow with teddy (in safe place?)—tries again to right table—has difficulty because table has caught in side of cot—persists—puts it right way up but endwise—watches ward maid with tea—tips table which goes over with bang—pulls it back—tries to turn it over—succeeds. Rubs head—watches ward maid with tea rather anxiously and tilts table

3.10 p.m.   —throws train on floor and watches for effect.

3.15 p.m.   Shows excitement as male nurse approaches with food—anxious again when nurse puts it down out of reach—is given food (pink custard and mug of milk)—looks disappointed and shows no eagerness to eat it. Plays with food—banging with

3.20 p.m.   spoon and stirring. Difficulty in holding spoon— changes hands—conveys some to mouth with difficulty. Nurse comes to feed him—refuses food, shakes head and cries. Nurse coaxes—cries and eats at same time. Drinks milk with an eye on the

3.25 p.m.   sweets placed near as bribe. Eats sweets.

Martin, was one year, five months. (It was not intended to observe children under two years, but Martin was near Kevin and the observer found him very interesting to watch.) Martin had been in hospital for a fortnight with an abscess in the groin. His mother visited each evening. He was sitting in his cot but fastened in by restrainers. His face was tear-stained and blotchy.

With only one or two momentary pauses Martin cried for the whole hour, plucking the fur from his teddy bear and eating it, or pulling at his penis. At one point the sister came and pulled his cot round so that he could see the television, but he ignored it and went on crying. When a ward maid spoke to him for a moment he stopped crying, but resumed with renewed vigour when she left him. He made several attempts to stand up but was hindered by his restrainers.

General hospital (P)
A children's ward in a general hospital. It was bright though old-fashioned and there was a quiet pleasant atmosphere, though the ward was exceedingly tidy. There were twenty beds for children up to thirteen years. Visiting was un-restricted. Three mothers were on the ward during the period of observation. There was one 'mother and child cubicle'. There was no air of bustle or strain on the ward but the children were rather left to their own devices. The children over five years had a teacher three mornings per week but there was no special provision made for the under-fives, and there were not many toys in evidence.

Sally, aged five years, had been in hospital for four days for repair of hernia. She was a quiet unsmiling child. She was 'up' in dressing-gown and pyjamas. Her mother had visited every day. She had no visitor at the time of observation.

11.00–11.30 a.m. Sits on bed of child whose mother is visiting —completely passive watching of mother and child playing together. Neither speaks nor joins in, nor shows any signs of animation, but does not look unduly unhappy.

11.30–11.55 a.m. Moves from bed to chair in centre of ward facing Observer. Sits very still watching and play-ing with dressing-gown cord. No attempt to make contact with any adult. No one speaks to her.

11.55 a.m. Goes silently to table for lunch at Nurse's request.

47

John, aged three years, seven months, had been in for three weeks for suspected Perthes' disease. He was an only child. Sister said that he was very 'good' when on his own but screamed and made a great fuss when mother came. In Sister's opinion mother spoiled him and had no control over him. He screamed 'Don't leave me!' when mother went but quietened down after only a few minutes. Mother visited daily.

11.00 a.m. Plays with beads. Wriggles. Adjusts socks. Drinks water. Rocks.

11.05 a.m. Tries to attract Observer's attention. Holds up snapshot—drops it over side of cot. Rocks. Calls 'I want to wee-wee'. Pushes toys around. Nurse brings urinal which he uses. Drinks orange juice

11.10 a.m. from tumbler on locker. Plays with empty tumbler, putting small toys and beads in—shows them to Nurse—who hands him a large toy rabbit. Shakes rabbit and makes attempt to undress it. Talks to mother visiting child opposite. Shakes

11.15 a.m. small toys in tumbler—turns them out and puts them in again—shakes—turns them out on to book—puts bricks in tumbler—tries to attract Observer's attention—tries to put foot in tumbler—continues experimenting with toys in and out of tumbler—shows them to Nurse—plays with sock,

11.20 a.m. gazing absently around him. Talks to Nurse. Soliloquizes, moving small toys around bed. Sings. Nurse takes away tumbler and fills it with orange juice—looks at tumbler in disgust as if to decide whether he can drink orange, makes to put toys in with sidewise glance at Nurse and desists. Pulls up socks—looks around—plays with water in jug on locker. Throws rabbit around cot. Plays with bricks—putting them in his mouth. Plays with

iv. Social contacts
are important

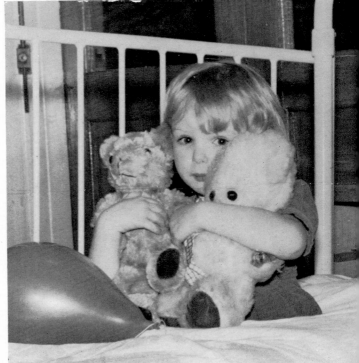

v. A plentiful
supply of toys is
not enough

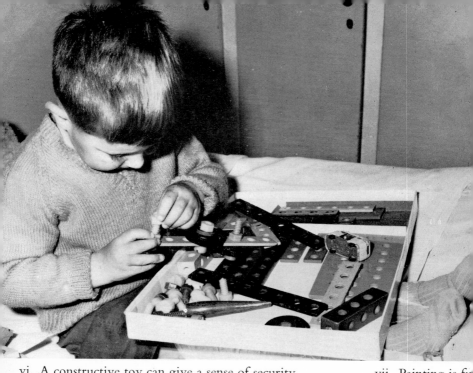

vi. A constructive toy can give a sense of security   vii. Painting is fu

shoulder straps of dungarees. Staff Nurse comes
11.25 a.m. and talks, encouraging him to make picture puzzle
with bricks. Staff Nurse departs—leaves bricks
and returns to small plastic toys. Picks up plastic
11.30 a.m. gun—pretends to shoot other child's mother, 'Oi,
Oi, Oi. Look at this. Look at me, Oi, quick'.
Shoots. 'There, you're dead. You come here and
I shoot you.' Nurse hushes him. 'Look at me I'm
going to shoot you. Cockadoodle doo!' Shoots
Observer. 'I'll shoot Doctor.' Sings. Throws gun
away. Pushes toys off cot-tray. Throws toys. Or-
11.35 a.m. derly reproves him with 'That's naughty'. 'No,
you're naughty!' Picks up gun again and throws
11.40 a.m. it down. Builds with bricks. Sings—'Staff, staff,
staff. Cockadoodledoo'. Throws toys on floor.
11.45 a.m. Back to brick building. Quiet concentration on
building. Pulls up socks. Calls 'Peter' to boy passing through ward. 'Want to wee-wee.' Nurse
takes him out of cot and to toilet. Comes back to
11.50 a.m. wash hands in basin on ward—splashes water—
reproved by nurse—dries hands—goes to sit at
11.55 a.m. table for lunch.

General Hospital (Q)

A surgical ward in the children's unit of a general hospital.
There was a main ward of ten beds for children up to thirteen
years and eight cubicles opening off a corridor, mainly for
infants. There was a reasonably well-equipped playroom.
Daily visiting was allowed except on the day of operation.
The ward and beds were very tidy and there were not many
toys in evidence. No provision of education or occupation
was made.

D

Mason, aged four years, was admitted the previous day for tonsillectomy. He was a bright, alert looking little boy.

10.15 a.m. Koala bear and rag-doll on bed—puts them in locker, takes them out of locker. Doctor turns from examination of next child and puts tray on Mason's locker in readiness. Waves doll and bangs doll's head on locker vigorously, bangs doll and bear together, throws them to end of bed, reaches them back—throws bear on floor and gives doll to child in next cot. Doctor returns. Talks to doctor, smiling and looks pleased—no apparent sign of

10.20 a.m. apprehension. Doctor examines—finishes—Mason sits up with pleased smile and takes a long time

10.25 a.m. buttoning up pyjama jacket. Tucks down in bed, wriggles, sits up to watch staff nurse with new admission. Nurse picks up bear from floor and

10.30 a.m. gives it to him—fingers bear and gazes around—throws bear on cot of next child—sits quietly

10.35 a.m. watching Mark (two and a half) on rocking-horse

10.40 a.m. in middle of ward—tucks down in bed. Sits up—watches. Yawns, rubs face, sucks finger—tucks down again—sits up watching nurse with trolley—tucks down and makes restless movements. Or-

10.45 a.m. derly polishing ward speaks to him—smiles and responds happily—sits up looking all around him. Pulls faces. Makes explosive noises. Mark comes

10.50 a.m. up to bed—suddenly comes to life laughing with Mark and penning him in with his locker. Hits Mark playfully—makes snarling animal noises—

10.55 a.m. plays 'push and shove' with David with locker—great glee as they both push locker in trial of strength—making snarling noises and shouting Bang! Bang! Orderly stops them, tucks Mason

11.00 a.m. tightly in bed and removes locker from reach. Talks to David (inaudible to Observer)—hangs out of bed. Picks up ear-phones and listens—puts down—makes animal noises at Mark who comes to his bed—suddenly bangs bed with fists vigor-
11.05 a.m. ously—laughter and simulated rough play with Mark. Orderly picks up Mark and puts him to bed. Leans out of bed to try to reach locker—staff nurse scolds him—sits back in bed looking sub-dued—sucks thumb—anxiously watches staff
11.10 a.m. nurse dismantling David's bed (David having been wheeled away in wheelchair). Sits sucking
11.15 a.m. fingers, anxiously looking around and rubbing ear.

David, aged three years, was admitted the previous day for tonsillectomy. A lively looking little boy.
10.15 a.m. Nurse carries back to bed from bathroom. Picks up teddy—smiles and waves it to and fro—talks to teddy—drinks orange—plays with sleeves of
10.20 a.m. pyjamas—watches doctor with Mason—looks out of window—talks to self (all talk inaudible)—
10.25 a.m. looks out of window—waves teddy and talks—watches new admission—holds teddy by foot waving to and fro—'loves' teddy. Spits on finger and marks on sheet—takes book from locker and puts back—shakes head—talks—pulls faces—looks
10.30 a.m. out of window—watches orderly polishing floor —reaches for locker—fingers teddy—counts fin-
10.35 a.m. gers—rocks teddy and talks—bangs teddy on bed
10.40 a.m. —'loves' teddy—bangs teddy on bed talking all the time—takes hanky from pocket—arranges hanky—waves teddy, puts teddy down. Looking

51

10.45 a.m. round ward anxiously. Talks to Mason—buttons
10.50 a.m. pyjamas—plays with pyjama buttons—'loves' teddy—rocks teddy. Rubs face. Orderly polishing
10.55 a.m. floor talks to him—shy response hiding behind teddy—shyness develops into game with orderly and playful hiding. Makes animal noises—talks to
11.00 a.m. Mason—Mark approaches—laughs and plays with him, hitting him and calling 'Come here'. Staff
11.05 a.m. nurse tells orderly to put Mark to bed (Mark resists and orderly leaves him). Suddenly very still and quiet and watchful. Talks to self. Suddenly bursts into animal noises and pushes locker towards Mason—plays 'push and shove' with locker with evident enjoyment—orderly removes locker —suddenly quiet and sucks fingers—pushes hands experimentally between bars of bed. Tentatively reaches towards locker but staff nurse comes to take him away (for treatment?).

General hospital (S)

A surgical ward of sixteen beds or cots in the children's wing of a large London hospital. The ward was very large, light and bright and there was a pleasant permissive atmosphere. Visiting was unrestricted, but mothers were encouraged to come in the afternoons. One mother was present in the morning.

There were a fair number of toys in evidence but no nursery nurses were employed and while there was an established school for the over-fives, the nursery-age group, which for ten years had been included in the school, had recently been officially excluded (by the Education Authority) much to the distress of the teachers who felt that this was a very important part of school in hospital. While they did their best in the time available to them, the staffing situation was such that they could not provide adequately both for the children they were officially appointed to teach and these little ones.

Steven, aged four years, had been in the ward for three days for investigation. A well-grown, sturdy child, he was standing on his bed, clad in pyjamas and dressing-gown, crying, when the observation began. He had on his bed three books, some biscuits, Potato Crisps, lollies and toilet articles.

10.45 a.m.   Wraps sweets in a piece of paper—puts them in his pocket—sits and whimpers.

10.50 a.m.   Stands, tying dressing-gown cord and putting his books inside his dressing-gown above it. Books drop out and he puts them back together with sweets, biscuits etc. from his bed. They drop

10.55 a.m.   again. He tears a page from his painting-book and uses this to wrap up his biscuits and sweets, whimpering quietly all the time. Stands up again and

11.00 a.m.   stows away his goods once more around his body inside his dressing-gown. A young doctor goes to talk to him but gets no response. The teacher comes and tidies biscuits and sweets from his bed into his locker. He allows her to do this but whim-

11.05 a.m.   pers and removes them all as soon as she goes away. He sits surrounded by them, eats a biscuit and watches another boy at the table playing with

11.10 a.m.   a farm. Shouts 'Stop it' when boy imitates dog barking. Teacher comes to talk to him—says 'I want to go home'. Teacher talks quietly to him for a moment and then leaves him. He climbs out of bed, picks things up from the floor and tucks them inside his pyjama jacket, pausing at times to watch the boy at the table. Ties cord of dressing-

53

11.15 a.m.	gown tight in an attempt to keep his possessions in his pyjamas. They all drop out and he patiently
11.20 a.m.	picks them up and starts again. Tries pushing books inside pyjama trousers but they all drop out
11.25 a.m.	and he cries. Gets back on bed, takes pyjama trousers off and tries to undo knot in cord, pulling
11.30 a.m.	at it with his teeth and whimpering. He succeeds, puts the trousers on again, and again tries to put the books in, but they drop out.

(Here the teacher left the ward taking the ambulant children with her which left the boy in the bed next to Steven, who had been doing school work, free to talk to him.)

11.35 a.m.	Gets out of bed and goes to next boy (older). Picks up boy's comics and talks to him. Wanders round, still looking lost, but whimpering has stopped. He goes back to his own bed, sitting on
11.40 a.m.	the stool by the side of it and watches the antics of the older boy in the next bed. Gets up and pushes the boy's bed in response to his request and talks to him (inaudible to Observer). Knives and forks are given out for dinner.

Ian, aged four years, who had been in for three weeks, had Perthes' disease and was on an extension, with his bed tipped up. The teacher reported that he took a long time to 'settle' and refused all toys at first. On his bedside table he had a farm with animals (given to him by teacher), tractor and car and a pair of plastic binoculars on his bed. He played with a number of things, not settling to anything for long though he appeared to be a happy little boy, chatting to porters, orderlies and nurses. He was constantly demanding attention, often dropping his toys in order to get it. He asked the teacher to give him the animals that the little girl in the next bed was playing with and was told that he must wait until she had finished with them, but a little later he persuaded a nurse to give him them.

Also observed here was a little Polish girl of three years, in a hip plaster, who had been in the ward three weeks and who understood no English. She lay very still sucking her thumb for ten minutes until the teacher gave her a box of wooden zoo animals. She lay smiling and putting these in and out of the box for twenty minutes until the nurse went to clean her up and gave the animals to Ian—when she made no protest but resorted to thumb-sucking and rolling her head on her pillow. She cried when the theatre porter came in with the trolley for another child.

General hospital (T)

A children's surgical ward in a large general hospital. This block was brightly decorated, light and airy, very well polished and tidy. There were flowers on the centre table of the ward of eight beds or cots, but no toys in evidence except for those on the children's beds and they were few in number. Each child had a very tidy locker. There was daily visiting, mainly afternoons and evenings, though mothers of small children were encouraged to go to feed them. The nursing staff were pleasant towards the children, but a little 'distant'. There was an almost unnatural quietness about the ward.

Gloria, aged three years, a very lively little West Indian girl, had been in for two days for tonsillectomy. Her parents visited in the evenings only, as they were working during the day. On her cot she had a naked plastic doll which cried when pressed.
2.05 p.m.   Sitting up in cot and showing Observer her dolly. Sucking her fingers, making noises, smiling and

55

talking to herself. Singing 'I got a dolly'. Makes doll cry. Lies down and sucks doll. Babbles against

2.10 p.m.   her fingers. Calls to Observer (unintelligible) and laughs. Stands doll up for Observer to see—rolls doll on cot—makes it walk—waves it to and fro. Rolls head on pillow—plays with fingers—twists her dress singing to herself. Nurse makes her bed and sits her up with doll tucked in beside her.

2.15 p.m.   Fingers doll, tosses it in the air. Rubs her head. Makes doll cry—jumps it up and down, clicking

2.20 p.m.   her tongue and gazing around her. Stands doll on its head—makes it squeak—hangs it on the side of the cot—licks it—smacks it—tries to get the squeaker out—presses hard on its tummy. Other

2.25 p.m.   children's mothers begin to arrive. Nurse comes and plays for one minute and then leaves. Looks longingly at little girl in next bed and her daddy. Squeezes doll vigorously so that it keeps up continuous crying—pauses to look round and then renews pressing of doll with vigorous rhythmic

2.30 p.m.   movement, rocking to and fro meanwhile. All the other children now have visitors. Gloria gazes at them bleakly. Looks anxiously at child returning from operation, sitting still and tensely, frozen in

2.35 p.m.   position. Puts sheets straight, watches door, picks at her arm, claps her hands, waves and smiles at mother and child on opposite side of ward, meanwhile making her doll cry loud and long. Freezes

2.40 p.m.   into sitting for a minute then rocks to and fro with her doll—tosses it over and over—makes it cry—clutches it and gazes at mother opposite. Throws doll down—rubs eyes—picks up doll again and

2.45 p.m.   jumps it up and down, making clicking noises—
56

presses its head in hard—stands it up and lets it fall —makes it jump on her knees—makes it cry—rocks—slaps doll—pokes at its eyes, handling it very roughly and looking fiercely at it. Sucks her fingers—clicks her tongue—yawns. Presses doll hard and fiercely making prolonged crying—washes doll's feet with spittle—swings it by the

2.50 p.m. feet, smacks it hard. Sucks her fingers. Smacks her doll. Looks enviously at daddy reading to girl in next bed. Sucks fingers—gazes wearily into space.

2.55 p.m. Pulls at her face—picks her nose—rubs her nose hard. Smiles and waves in response to wave from another child's mother. Picks vigorously at nose, her expression becoming more and more bereft as

3.00 p.m. time goes on. Gazes round blankly turning head to look at door occasionally. Nurse goes to speak to her but gets no response. Waves doll, gazing into space and fingering it in a desultory fashion.

Play supervised by mothers of 'in-patients'

Teaching hospital (I)
A children's ward in a well-known teaching hospital. It was small and somewhat dark but there was a pleasant friendly atmosphere. The majority of the patients were infants being nursed in separate cubicles but there were four toddlers under five and one boy of seven on the main ward. Visiting was allowed from 10 a.m. to 7 p.m. There were three mothers on the ward with their children during the observation. There were no 'mothers-in' facilities.

There were plenty of toys easily accessible to the 'up' children and apart from one very sick child they were all up. No nursery nurses were employed as matron likes her nurses to

57

get as much experience of handling children as possible. Mothers of 'in-patients' supervised play.

Ian, aged three and a half years, who had a club foot, was waiting to go home in plaster.

2.40 p.m.	Sitting quietly at table in ward, beside Neil, who is sitting on his mother's lap. Playing with 'Bildit' —quietly and solemnly building up and taking to pieces. No visible signs of emotion.
2.55 p.m.	Mother comes with clothes to take him home. Smiles and tears together—trembling—but not clinging. Whimpering while being dressed. Tea
3.00 p.m.	brought in—refuses to have any. Anxious to go. Departs, still hovering between smiles and tears.

Neil, aged three years, had chronic constipation due to mal-formation of bowel. He had a history of frequent hospitaliza-tion. His mother visited daily from 2 p.m. to 7 p.m. She said that he made no fuss about coming to hospital himself but showed more signs of upset when she herself was admitted to hospital. A very thin, pale, lethargic-looking child.

2.40 p.m.	Sitting on mother's lap building with plastic bricks ('Bildit') whining when mother turns her
2.45 p.m.	attention from him to other children or mothers.
2.50 p.m.	Tea brought in—goes on building. 'Don't touch that building, that's a house'—refuses tea and goes
3.00 p.m.	on building. Mother tries to coax him to have tea —refuses—continues building.
3.05 p.m.	Building.
3.10 p.m.	Begins to eat tea—mother feeds and coaxes.
3.15 p.m.	Eating tea.
3.20 p.m.	Tea finished—returns to building—rather aim-lessly and listlessly picking up and putting down

bricks but allows mother to talk to other mothers without interruption, though still remaining on

3.25 p.m. her knee. Picks up small plastic toy Indian and puts it on building—pushing building around as if

3.30 p.m. a vehicle, but without vocalizing. Walks Indian up and down building. Puts Indian down. Continues building. Pulls building apart and puts

3.35 p.m. bricks in basket—takes bricks out of basket and starts to build again. Demands his mother's help.

3.40 p.m. Leaves mother's knee and fetches more bricks.

3.45 p.m. Takes building apart and puts in box. Takes out and builds again—packs up again—takes box

3.50 p.m. away—walks round ward—back to mother's lap —playing with Indians. Talking to mother and demanding her full attention. Tries to eat left-over sandwich—mother prevents and gives sweets. Goes to toilet accompanied by mother.

3.55 p.m. Returns. Asks mother to read book. Asks mother

4.00 p.m. to lift him on to rocking-horse—wants to be pushed. Mother refuses and he rocks himself until Observer talks to mother, when he whines and wants to climb down. Back on mother's lap at table reading book. Makes a fuss over having

4.05 p.m. temperature taken.

Teaching hospital (L)

The children's medical ward of a well-known London teaching hospital with twelve beds in the main ward and some cubicles for infants. The ward was somewhat enclosed but there was a large bright playroom, supervised by mothers of in-patients, to which all ambulant children might go and occasionally a child in a cot was taken in. There was a large balcony outside the playroom on to which the children could go in fine weather. Unrestricted visiting was allowed on this ward, four mothers being present at the time of observation.

A peripatetic teacher could be called in for children over eight years but no provision was made for those under eight. No nursery nurses were employed and the nurses in training did only eight weeks on the children's wards.

Eileen, aged four years, who had been hospitalized for twenty-three months with diseased bone. Eileen, who was the thirteenth child in a family of fourteen, was infrequently visited. She had been sent to a long-stay hospital where there was a hospital school, but it was found that her family did not visit at all and for fear that she should grow away from them altogether she was brought back to London, where she was more easily accessible. She was lying on her tummy on a frame with a large tray of toys in front of her. A young almoner was with her at the beginning of the observation.

10.30 a.m. Chatting to almoner and drawing on her pad. Almoner tears off page of drawing and gives it to Eileen before departing. Eileen folds up the draw-
10.35 a.m. ing and lies holding it, gazing around. Questions Observer as to what she is doing—bites pen and
10.40 a.m. looks around her—scribbles on case—bangs with pen—props head on hand—raises herself up to look around—opens case and looks inside—shuts
10.45 a.m. it again. Examines Biro—pulls at end of it—plays with catch of attaché case—sighs—yawns—calls nurse—bangs folded paper between hands—looks
10.50 a.m. at Observer and invitingly—calls nurse who answers 'Just a minute'. Picks up naked doll, folds cloth and puts it on as a nappie—seeks around bed (for fastener?). Asks orderly if she may go to the playroom—props arm on doll and gazes longingly

10.55 a.m. in direction of playroom. Nurse wheels her cot into playroom and she watches through the bars two boys sitting on the floor building with large bricks. Continues watching, rather wistfully, as

11.00 a.m. boys chase madly round playroom. Calls 'Andrew's mummy—come and sit by me'. 'Take

11.05 a.m. your coat off and I'll hold it for you. Why do you keep it on?', reaching out and touching. 'Aren't they naughty—they running away down the

11.10 a.m. ward' (boys). Waits sadly for Andrew's mother to settle by her. Leans head on hand, gazing around. 'Will you read me a story, Andrew's mummy?'. Shows mother a story-book. Mother has to leave her to comfort her own child, who has fallen. Eileen turns over pages of her book lethargically. Mother returns to look at book with her, but again has to leave because her own child throws a temper tantrum. Eileen lies sucking her fingers,

11.15 a.m. pulling her tongue and licking her hand while mother tries to persuade Andrew to share book and suggests that she sits where Eileen can hear her reading to Andrew. Eileen protests, 'I want you right close'. Andrew goes off and mother begins to read to her. Andrew screams and mother again

11.20 a.m. has to leave Eileen who makes no protest but looks sad. Mother returns and continues story—Eileen reaches out, touches her and holds her hand. Andrew again demands attention and mother moves away. Eileen asks for dolly which mother gives her, together with a bag of clothes. Accepts with

11.25 a.m. pleasure but does not play. Leans on side of cot looking wistful—sucks thumb—reaches out to mother. Looks into bag and takes out doll's

61

	clothes. Asks mother for another doll and announces with great pleasure 'This is a new dolly. I've got a new dolly! I've found a new dolly
11.30 a.m.	here!'. Shows doll to Observer and with encouragement chooses dress to put on, but asks Observer to do it for her.

At the end of the hour Observer talked to and played with Eileen for a little while. Eileen wrote a 'letter' to her mummy on Observer's pad and asked her to be sure to give it to the postman. Eileen had the facile approach to strangers typical of a much hospitalized deprived child.

Teaching hospital (M)

A children's ward, both medical and surgical, with twelve beds or cots, in a large well-known teaching hospital. The ward was large, bright and airy with a pleasant air of busyness, an abundance of toys scattered around and several mothers were sitting with their children. Visiting was completely unrestricted and mothers were encouraged to help both with their own and other children. The 'up' children were running around freely. The sister was very much aware of the children's needs and would have appreciated having a play therapist. A teacher came for two hours each morning for children over five years who were to be hospitalized for more than three weeks.

William, aged three years, suffering from a congenital heart defect, had been in hospital for several weeks. He came from a large poor family and was visited infrequently. The staff, both nursing and domestic, appeared to be very fond of him and he made contact with many but did not seem to be attached to any particular one. He was very mischievous and Sister said that he was quite indifferent to scolding or punishment. He was an undersized, pale little boy, but very active.

2.30 p.m. In kitchen with orderlies who blow up a balloon for him. Steals a biscuit from the trolley being prepared for tea and is shooed out into the ward,

2.35 p.m. where he runs around showing his balloon to visi-

2.40 p.m. tors and examining other children's toys. Runs aimlessly back and forth, into the corridor, into the sluice, into the bathroom clutching his balloon

2.45 p.m. but not playing with it. There are two little boys of four and five years playing with cars but William ignores them. Runs off into corridor and is brought back by Sister, who gives him a large

2.50 p.m. plastic wheelbarrow in which he trundles his balloon down the ward, but soon abandons it. Joins mother and little girl and examines her toys. Takes large torch from tray on Sister's table and experiments, shining the light through his balloon. Puts torch back on request and runs off down

2.55 p.m. corridor. Nurse brings him back—holding him in her arms, playing with him and cuddling him— takes him out to change wet pants. Runs back— takes Observer's umbrella and runs around ward with it, pushing a tissue along the floor with the ferrule. Runs off down corridor and orderly brings him back, returns umbrella. Rescues his balloon

3.00 p.m. from another boy. Vanishes down corridor. Returns. Tries to raid another little girl's locker but thwarted by her mother. Fingers cakes on tea-trolley which has just been wheeled in. Rescues balloon again and tries to put it on his cot, climbing on a chair to do so. Falls in climbing off chair and whimpers—orderly, whom he calls 'Auntie',

3.05 p.m. picks him up, comforts him and sits him at table

63

for tea, where he sits sucking his thumb. Nurse gives him tea and he tucks in hungrily for a moment or two then asks 'Can I get my balloon?'. Orderly tells him to finish tea. Addresses another child's mother as mummy. Gets up from table and runs around—goes to another child's locker, runs

3.10 p.m. off down corridor. Comes back to finish tea—walks around, eating a sandwich—nurse brings him back to the table and watches him finish his tea. Laughs and teases nurse, 'playing her up'.

3.15 p.m. Finishes tea, runs to get book from cot. Says 'Mummy, I can't do this', to a mother sitting by the table. Walks round with book and shows it to another mother. Runs away down corridor. Comes back to the ward—plays with light switches. Takes a beaker of orange juice from a little girl's locker and drinks some before the

3.20 p.m. mother takes it away from him. Tips the contents out of a truck and wheels it down the ward, then abandons it. Urinates on the floor and goes away to tell nurse who brings him back to change his

3.25 p.m. pants. Borrows 'Jack in a box' belonging to another boy, with mother's permission—she shows him how to work it—spends four minutes ab-

3.30 p.m. sorbed in it—mother demonstrates again how it works. Shows it to nurse and says 'No!' very firmly to another boy who wants to play with it.

Connie, a little Cypriot girl aged four years, was a post-meningitis case, who spoke no English. She had been in hospital several days. Her mother stayed with her all day at first but at this time only came in the evening. Sister said that she was a difficult child, throwing things and spitting at people, but that

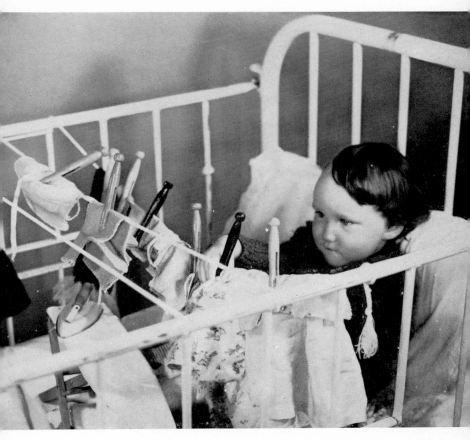

viii. 'This is the way Mummy does it'

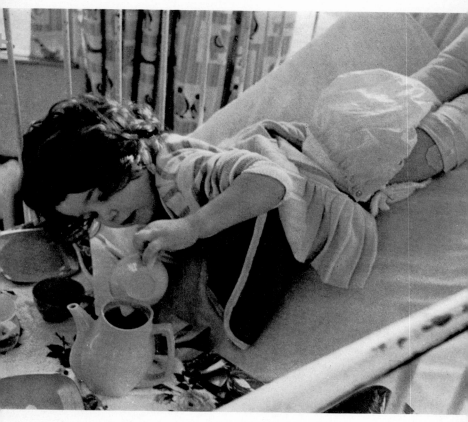

ix. Play goes on in spite of a difficult position

she could be very sweet. Her sombre little face wore a defensive look.

2.30 p.m. Standing looking over side of cot, which has an extension on the sides so that she cannot possibly climb out. Tries to throw her bed-table at nurse,

2.35 p.m. who removes it. Watches little boy from next cot sitting on his mother's lap, sadly pulling at cot

2.40 p.m. sides. Smiles at a boy as he passes her cot. Throws book after him followed by a box (now nothing left on her bed). Points to toy on next child's bed

2.45 p.m. and speaks, obviously asking for it. The mother says no, she will only throw it at someone. Spits at

2.50 p.m. the mother. Lies on tummy with head on hand, gazing in front of her. Kneels up at end of cot making noises. Stands and looks longingly over

2.55 p.m. cot side. Looks at tea-trolley just wheeled in but

3.00 p.m. makes no sound. Nurse brings cot-tray—responds

3.05 p.m. with happy smile—helps to fix it, sits down quietly and eats her tea with her back to the other

3.10 p.m. children, looking rather lonely and isolated. Stands up with cake in her hand watching other children over the end of the cot. Eats the cake.

3.15 p.m. Crawls round cot. Claps her hands. Crouches and looks through bars. Rolls herself up into a ball.

3.20 p.m. Stands and looks over the sides, with her foot on the cot-tray, pushing crockery aside with her foot. Points to toys on next cot and asks but again refused. Shakes bars of cot and threatens to throw her plate but gives it up readily to nurse. Stands on

3.25 p.m. cot-table and swings. Calls for nurse showing great distress—smiles when nurse picks her up and takes her to the toilet. Struggles a little when nurse tries to put her back in her cot but laughs with her

E

and obediently lies down while nurse takes a rectal temperature—playing with nurse's hand. Nurse leaves.

3.30 p.m.   Shakes cot sides, throws pillow out, kicks locker, rolls herself into a ball, stands and points at toy on next bed. Mother of next child passes her a plastic tractor and she sits down examining it with great pleasure, making contented noises. Pulls the driving-wheel off and tries to put it back—fails—throws it on floor. Does the same with rear wheels.

General hospital (R)

A children's unit in a general hospital, where mothers were encouraged to stay with children under five, eight cubicles being available for this. The mothers were made welcome and comfortable, allowed to care for their children as much as possible, and given support when they needed it by an understanding sister. The children whose mothers were not able to stay with them and those over five years were accommodated in the main ward containing, on the day of observation, nine beds and cots. Completely free visiting was allowed here. There was a very happy atmosphere, plenty of toys and a very well-equipped playroom with sand-trays, dolls' houses and wheeled toys. On the day on which these observations were made there was no one to attend to the play needs of the three young children on the ward but the sister was well aware of these needs and made use of the cadets who came on other days, for this purpose. The mothers helped to feed other children but did not appear to look after their play needs.

The children over five years had a visiting teacher.

Christopher, aged two and a half years, had been in the ward for four days for repair of hernia. He could have gone home but his mother had said that she was not able to cope with him. It was hoped that he would go home that day. Sister reported that he made little response to anyone. He had on his bed a teddy bear, a plastic bus and a plastic bottle.

10.45 a.m. Lying on his back, clutching teddy bear and bus. Sucking bottle continuously. Fingering teddy, gazing round rather vacantly.

10.50 a.m. Shaking cot side. Rubbing hair, running his fingers through it—fingering his ear—clutching bus and teddy. Fingering bus—rubbing hair—finger-

10.55 a.m. ing pillow—fingering bus—rubbing hair—renewed vigour in sucking bottle—watching a boy

11.00 a.m. having walking exercises—holding side of cot with one hand and clutching bus in other. Doctor examining another child greets him but no res-

11.05 a.m. ponse or apparent reaction apart from further vigorous rubbing of hair. Restless moving of arms

11.10 a.m. —sighing—rolling head but no other change of

11.15 a.m. position—watches by moving head and eyes only —takes bottle from mouth and gives a little cry to

11.20 a.m. attract orderly's attention—calls 'More'. Orderly

11.25 a.m. replies 'In a minute'. Puts empty bottle back in mouth and fingers hair. Restless movement of

11.30 a.m. arms and rubbing hair—sighs—rolls head—

11.35 a.m. whimpers—follows another child's mother around with his eyes—pulls at his pillow—fingers bus,

11.40 a.m. apathetically—turns wheels—whimpers and calls

11.45 a.m. out something unintelligible.

Rupert, aged five years, was in for tonsillectomy. He had his operation the previous day. His mother was not able to get off from work to be with him but visited in the evening. He appeared to be rather a serious, anxious little boy.

10.45–11.05 a.m. Sleeping.

11.05–11.10 a.m. Doctor with him.

11.10 a.m. Sits up in bed gazing around rather sadly. Tucks down into bed again with his rabbit. Nurse takes temperature. Fidgetting around in his bed—

11.15 a.m. watching Observer—sucking fingers—lying star-

11.20 a.m. ing into space. Orderly asks if he would like a

11.25 a.m. book—shakes head—moves restlessly—turns over

11.30 a.m. —sits up and looks around. Staff nurse comes and

11.35 a.m. says 'Mummy rang up and sends her love. She's going to ring again this afternoon so that you can talk to her'. Obvious attempt to control tears—

11.40 a.m. lies down and hides head.

Later on in the afternoon Observer sat down and talked to him and read him a story which he seemed to enjoy and was loath to let her go.

Susan, aged three years, was hospitalized for diet regulation but was also receiving psychiatric treatment. She was said to be an affectionless child.

10.45 a.m. In cubicle with another child and his mother, handling his toys. Runs into main ward, to a locker—opens and shuts door with a bang. Runs

10.50 a.m. to orderly and away again. Runs round ward.

10.55 a.m. Goes to locker and takes out comic and takes it to the playroom then out again and wanders off down the corridor singing and waving her comic. Returns to ward. Goes into playroom. Wanders

11.00 a.m. round singing. Stands in middle of ward sucking

11.05 a.m. plastic toy. Goes to talk to older girl in bed. Goes

11.10 a.m. into playroom. Returns with toy car which she shows to girl in bed. Runs down corridor, back,

11.15 a.m. out to playroom. Comes back into the ward. Climbs on a chair by table—down again and away

11.20 a.m. down corridor. Comes running back waving a

11.25 a.m. piece of paper. Goes out to playroom and begins playing with doll's house. Runs back into ward

11.30 a.m. and takes off her cardigan which she swings around and then puts on her bed. Picks up a basket from her locker and runs off down the corridor with it on her head, singing. Follows another

11.35 a.m. child's mother into the ward and then out into the playroom. Comes back to her locker. Puts her cardigan away in locker. Shows Observer her dress. Goes back to playroom and plays briefly

11.40 a.m. with other children there. Returns to ward and takes a card from her locker. Walks around

11.45 a.m. waving card and singing.

Nursery nurses employed for general child-care duties including play

Children's hospital (B)

A general medical ward in a large modern children's hospital. The ward, which accommodated eight children, was light, bright and airy and there was a happy permissive atmosphere. The children's ages ranged from nineteen months to eleven years. Visiting was unrestricted, one mother being present at the time of observation. There was a well-equipped playroom along the corridor and the 'up' children were roaming freely in and out. There were few suitable toys in evidence on the ward. There was a school, provided by the Education Authority, for children over five years, but the under-fives were catered for by a nursery nurse whose duties included supervising the children's general well-being, their clothes

69

and their play. The nursery nurse on this ward had been doing the work for six weeks only and although she said she found the work very interesting, apart from keeping an eye on the children running around, she made little contribution to their play needs, as the following observation shows.

Jane, aged three years, was admitted six days previously for the second time. She was a chubby little girl, sitting very quietly and seriously in her cot with a cot-tray in front of her on which there was a colouring-book and a pencil-case containing coloured pencils. She had one other book on her cot, but no toys. Her locker was within reach. Her mother visited daily.

11.10 a.m.	Sitting fingering pencils and gazing around. Puts pencils away in case and sits looking rather sad and pale, rubbing her head from time to time. Pulls off her sock and puts it back on again two or three
11.15 a.m.	times. Sits looking around in a dull and lifeless way. Picks up her pencil-case again, opens it and
11.20 a.m.	examines the pencils lethargically. Puts pencils away, turns over and buries her head in her pillow, face down. Asks nursery nurse for a drink and smiles when given it. Lies down and plays with socks again—turns over and buries head in pillow.
11.25 a.m.	Sits up and looks around, lies down again, rolling and fidgetting. Two boys come in from the
11.30 a.m.	schoolroom shouting 'Here!'. Jane apparently takes no notice, but a second later re-echoes 'Here!'. Rolls body around cot with head still buried in pillow, talking inaudibly. Singing, waving legs, and talking to herself—mostly inaudibly,
11.35 a.m.	though at one point the words 'No!, No!, No!' come through. Ignores other children running

11.40 a.m. round ward. Looks round at sound of nurse's voice. Ward is suddenly full of bustle and activity but Jane shows little response until an orderly comes and speaks to her and plays with her, when she raises an apathetic smile and kicks her legs.

11.45 a.m. The nursery nurse goes to talk to her about her colouring-book. Jane sits up and becomes quite animated, pointing out the pictures in her book and counting with the nurse. Starts, with nursery

11.50 a.m. nurse's encouragement, to colour her book, but the moment nursery nurse leaves her, sinks back into her former apathetic state, only brightening up on her return. Nursery nurse gives her another drink. Jane picks up her other book and begins to show it. Nursery nurse turns aside and Jane bangs the book on the cot-tray, smiling when nursery nurse looks at her. Looks at book, talking and waving it up and down. Leans head on hand wearily, still turning pages in a desultory manner.

11.55 a.m. Throws book down and pushes table away. Rolls over on pillow, hides face and lies waving her legs and rubbing her feet along the edge of the cot-tray, showing no reaction when another child

12 noon cries. When the nursery nurse returns Jane rolls over and looks hopefully towards her, but when

12.05 p.m. she takes no notice of her, turns back to her pillow.

12.10 p.m. Nurse comes to take her to the playroom for lunch.

Also observed here was *Karen, aged nineteen months,* in for investigation, who was sitting near Jane in a baby's chair, clutching a bottle of orange juice. She had a football annual on the tray in front of her and for the whole hour she sucked the bottle, occasionally flipped over the pages of the book, tore off pieces of paper and ate them, gazing round in a bewildered manner. The only time she received any attention was when she soiled and needed cleaning up.

Peter, aged two and a half years, who had been in for five and a half weeks for investigation, appeared quite happily at home and ran busily around, investigating everything in typical two-year-old fashion. His mother came half-way through the morning.

Teaching hospital (O)

The children's ward in a well-known general hospital. It was a bright, gaily decorated, bungalow-type building in pleasant grounds. The ward was divided into cublicles by glass partitions, some cubicles holding four beds and some just one. The ages of the children ranged from a few months to twelve years.

There was a pleasant easy atmosphere and while the ward was tidy and well polished it was not excessively so. The children had access to their lockers and their toys were kept in tidy-bags on the ends of their beds, where not all of them could reach. There was a day-room with a plentiful supply of toys to which 'up' children had free access, but there were some children with no toys on their beds.

There was unrestricted visiting but there were no mothers in the morning and only three in the afternoon.

Two nursery nurses were employed on this ward, one part-time and one full-time. From conversation with the one on duty it was obvious that her function was considered to be mainly a nursing one, i.e. feeding, washing and toilet, and that she had little time for playing. Indeed she did not seem to consider this an important part of her duties. There were two teachers catering for the needs of school-age children.

CHILDREN OBSERVED

Four children aged four years and nine months, four years and six months, five and four, were observed for twenty minutes before lunch but time samples were not taken.

They were well supplied with the kinds of toys brought in by parents, i.e. dolls, teddy bears, plastic soldiers and indians, small bricks and mechanical toys and comics, but did not play with any degree of concentration with these. There was some imaginative group play about being piggies wanting their dinner. They all chatted easily to Observer—though Caroline, aged four years and six months, was much quieter than the others and appeared a little anxious. (She had had a tonsillectomy.) These children were free to get on and off their beds and roam around.

Tracey, aged four years, had had a small skin graft on her forehead. She had been in two days and had her operation the previous day. In the morning she had been noticed standing on her bed and looking through the glass partition at the four children under observation (she was in a single cubicle).

1.25 p.m.	Nothing whatsoever on bed. Sits on edge of bed staring and biting thumb—watches boy going down ward with mechanical toy. Fiddles with paper bag hanging on locker (for rubbish). Stands on pillow and watches other children through glass partition. Turns attention back to paper bag —stands up again and looks through partition.
1.30 p.m.	Stands — sits — stares — clicks tongue — sighs — shakes bed—rubs ear—dangles legs over bedside
1.35 p.m.	—sighs—smiles at orderly removing cover from bed—tells orderly her age and name—gets into bed (i.e. under bedclothes)—stares—gets back on

73

1.40 p.m.	top of bedclothes. Nurse comes to take temperature—submits passively—gets under bedclothes again—gazes blankly around—on top of bed again
1.45 p.m.	—watches through screen—back into bed—rubs eyes, sighs—fiddles with paper bag—stands up to look through partition—back to paper bag—pulls
1.50 p.m.	faces—gets back under bedclothes—leans head on
1.55 p.m.	hand—lies down—stares—sighs—lies very still—
2.00 p.m.	turns over—lies quietly. Turns over at sound of
2.05 p.m.	nurse's voice—sleeps.

Stephen, aged three and a half years, had been in for three weeks for appendicectomy. He had been up but a slight relapse had sent him back to bed. His mother visited daily.

At the beginning of the observation he was looking at a book and talking softly to himself. He turned the pages over in a listless way for five minutes then dropped the book on the floor and sat looking around him, pulling his lip, playing with his fingers and sucking his thumb. He smiled and responded when a nurse came and gave him a plastic car from his toy-bag and played with him for a minute or two, but relapsed into aimless twiddling of wheels when she left him. Eventually he pulled them off and broke them, saying 'Take it home and mend it. When's mummy coming?'. Mother arrived shortly afterwards and he greeted her happily.

A nursery nurse employed as a full-time play therapist

Teaching hospital (K)
A surgical ward in a well-known teaching hospital. The ward, which was in three divisions, each containing seven beds or cots, was bright and cheerful, well supplied with toys and there was evidence of a child-centred attitude behind the or-

ganization. There was a pleasant permissive atmosphere with
a certain amount of homely untidiness. Here a nursery nurse
was employed purely for 'play therapy'. The nursing staff also
took an interest in the children's occupations and Sister said
that they considered this an important part of their work
when the play lady was not on duty. A teacher came in two
hours per day for the over-fives who were going to be hospitalized for more than three weeks. When the weather was
fine as many children as possible were taken out on to the
green. There was practically free visiting, but parents were
not encouraged to come in the morning.

All the children appeared to be happily occupied, there was
an air of contentment on the ward and there were friendly
contacts between children and staff.

Juliet, aged four years, who had been in for two weeks, had
both legs encased in plaster. A friendly little girl who appeared to make instant contact with everyone. She had a
jigsaw puzzle and a soft toy on her bed.

10.20 a.m. 'Play Lady' gives her a large tin of brightly coloured beads and a threader and she becomes absorbed in making a necklace for herself. She has
her temperature taken and chats to the nurse about
10.25 a.m. her beads. Nurse goes away and Juliet returns to
10.30 a.m. her bead-threading, pausing only to watch Andrew practising walking. Is completely absorbed
in her bead-threading. Is encouraged by Sister to
10.35 a.m. drink her orange juice—returns to beads announc-
10.45 a.m. ing 'nearly done'. Calls 'Play Lady'. Tries necklace
round her neck—calls to Michael to look. 'Play
10.50 a.m. Lady' returns and helps her to fasten necklace and
suggests that she finish another one already
started. Goes on threading beads but stops to

75

10.55 a.m.   watch Mark having a blood-test, looking very
              alarmed and shouting 'I'm not having one'. Feels
11.00 a.m.   and examines her own fingers while watching
              Mark having his 'pricked'. Lies back wearily and
              rubs her head. Sits up when 'Play Lady' appears
11.05 a.m.   with paints for Michael. 'Can I paint?' 'Play Lady'
              removes beads—Sister lifts Juliet out of bed and
11.10 a.m.   puts her at the table. 'Play Lady' gives her paper
11.15 a.m.   and paints and she sets to work, becoming com-
11.20 a.m.   pletely absorbed.

Marie, aged three and a half years, had been in three days this
time, but had a record of frequent hospitalizations. 'Play Lady'
said that she always returned knowing exactly what she
wanted to do. She had had her operation the day before and
was still a little dazed but had decided that a story was her
right and insisted on this.

10.20–10.35 a.m. Listening quite contentedly to a story.
10.40 a.m.   Asks 'Play Lady' for a raffia mat and lies back
  to   happily when promised 'in a minute'. Sits up in
10.55 a.m.   alarm when Mark has a blood-test. 'I'm not going
              to have one, Play Lady!' (a real distress signal).
11.00 a.m.   'Play Lady' brings raffia mat which she begins to
11.05 a.m.   do, but falls asleep in the doing.

Also observed were Michael, a rather difficult five-year-old,
who was very restless and demanding, and Mark, aged three
and a half, who appeared to be a very happy, friendly little
boy, always absorbed in the task of the moment. 'Play Lady'
coped with all in a quiet unruffled manner, always there 'on
demand'.

Nursery teachers supervise play

Children's hospital (C)

A medical ward in a children's hospital. It was an old-fashioned building, but the wards were bright and cheerful and ambulant children were running around freely. There was a pleasant permissive atmosphere full of busyness. There was a school, and children were doing clay modelling, playing skittles and cutting out. Nursery nurses were employed for non-medical duties and played with the children when time permitted. There was unrestricted visiting.

William, aged four years, three months, was admitted two days previously with a head injury (not serious). He was lying in his cot, holding a plastic aeroplane and a bus. A very bright, alert-looking little boy.

1.45 p.m.	Teacher comes and sits him up, gives him a cot-table and a construction toy. Responds with a smile, saying 'I know how to build. I have one of these at home'. Begins to build, breaks off to look
1.50 p.m.	with concern at another boy taking medicine—turns back to his building apparently quite absorbed but with a hint of more than natural intensity. Builds a tall tower, looks at it with a
1.55 p.m.	pleased smile, talks to doctor about it—calls out cheerfully to any approaching adult.
2.00 p.m.	Dismantles tower and begins building a house. Nurse comes to take him to be weighed. Returns and goes back to his building, explaining it to the
2.05 p.m.	teacher when she goes to speak to him. Does not appear to take much notice of the other children. 'I'm making a train' (to doctor). Packs up bricks in
2.10 p.m.	box. 'I builded something' (to sister). Picks up bus

77

2.15 p.m.   and pushes it round his table—leans back and looks around a little wistfully—Registrar approaches with a group of students—looks at them, wheeling bus frantically up and down table.

2.17–2.45 p.m.   Completely surrounded by students to whom Registrar is demonstrating. At first William ignores them playing in a rather feverish way with his plane, then stops playing and listens, joining in with their laughter once or twice. As time goes on his behaviour becomes increasingly babyish. He is making noises, pulling faces and playing with a student's hand. He does not cry or make a fuss but his face becomes increasingly flushed. His mother comes in at 2.40 p.m. and he smiles and waves to her but makes no move towards her. Towards the end of the session he begins to rub his eyes and make restless movements. When the students have finished his mother comes and he gives her a big hug.

2.50 p.m.   Mother goes off and William lies back in his cot hugging his plane and bus. Sister comes and sits him up and gives him back his table and bricks—begins to build, making noises and pulling faces. Mother returns and produces a new toy over which he exclaims happily. Plays with new toy, but at the same time continues to hug the old.

Also on this ward was *Fanny, aged four years, seven months,* who had a long history of frequent hospitalization, though this time her admission was due to a road accident. She was encropetic (soiling) and enuretic, a volatile restless child with very poor speech, whose mother said that she just could not cope with her.

78

After a short period of restless wandering she settled down for half an hour to some cutting out and pasting which the teacher encouraged her to do. Next she went to look at a book with another child, and then joined in a story session with the teacher and a group of children.

Children's long-stay hospital (G)

An orthopaedic hospital catering for 120 children, many of whom were long-stay cases. The hospital was out in the country and the bungalow-type wards were scattered over extensive grounds. There was a solarium outside each ward, on to which the beds were pushed in fine weather. There was an established school where special attention was paid to the needs of nursery children. Daily visiting was allowed, the time being left to the discretion of each ward sister. Ward one accommodated twenty-eight children from nil to ten years. Two teachers were employed here, one junior/infant and one nursery trained. Ward two had twelve cots for children under five. One nursery teacher was employed here. A pleasant permissive atmosphere pervaded and there was a homely untidiness about the wards. The children were given normal nursery school occupations.

Helen, aged three years, had been in hospital nine days. She had congenitally deformed hips and was in plaster to her waist. She was lying on her tummy. A rather pale, anxious-looking child.

9.30 a.m. Bed-making in progress and Sister has put another child on Helen's bed, but she is not taking any notice—she is rather pale and anxious looking—picking her nose—watching the teacher on her
9.35 a.m. way round the ward with toy-trolley. Rather
9.40 a.m. heavy-eyed and a weary look. Nurse tries to give

79

her some medicine—cries and turns head away.
Nurse tries to persuade, fails and leaves medicine
on locker. Hides face. Teacher goes with toy-
9.45 a.m. trolley—whimpers and talks in whining voice—
teacher goes on talking quietly to her as she picks
up book brought by mummy and talks about it—
Helen smiles and responds by showing 'get well'
cards to teacher. 'Look what I got'—shows teacher
9.50 a.m. drawing-book. Teacher gives board and crayons
—Helen chats happily and starts in busily with
crayons quiet and absorbed—with tongue out.
Watches sister and theatre orderly rather anxiously
—pulling at tongue. Returns to crayoning—waving free foot to and fro. Looks around—teacher
approaches and Helen talks about drawing.
10.00 a.m. Teacher spreads plastic cover on bed and gives
bowl of sand, funnel, sieve, bucket and wooden
spoon. Stirs sand with wooden spoon—pours
through funnel, holds funnel and gazes around
ward with faintly worried air. Examines funnel—
rolls grains of sand between fingers—puts face in
10.05 a.m. funnel and sings, experimenting with putting funnel at different distances from face. Watches sister,
glances at medicine on locker, bites lips—gazes
10.10 a.m. around—returns to playing with sand—pours
sand from bottle to sieve—scooping up sand—
happily smiling and absorbed—scoops sand—
pours from bottle through sieve—experimenting
with sieve in different positions—talking to self—
10.15 a.m. smiling and apparently oblivious of surroundings
—stirring—pouring—squeezing sand between
fingers—filling bucket—turning bucket over—
10.20 a.m. experimenting with spoon. Tries to attract

x. Sand and water promote long periods of settled play

xi. Playing out hospital procedures

xii. Music not only gives pleasure but has great therapeutic value

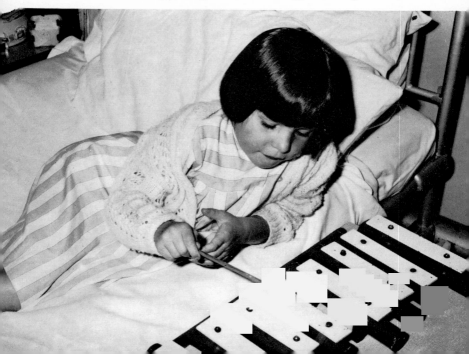

teacher's attention and points to table—sad look
10.25 a.m. returns. 'I've finished now', 'I want something else' (rather whiny voice). Teacher helps her to clear up sand. Points to table and teacher gives her three bears and case of clothes. Examines bears—opens case—takes out clothes and proceeds to
10.30 a.m. dress and undress bears with great absorption.

Wendy, aged three years, ten months, had dislocated hips. She had been in hospital for four months. Her mother visited very rarely. She showed signs of bodily ill-treatment when she was admitted, was terrified of bathing and screamed hysterically when moved. The teacher said that she had only recently begun to laugh and talk spontaneously. She appeared to be a happy healthy child.

9.45 a.m. Teacher spreads plastic sheets on bed and gives bowl with water. Experiments with plastic bottles and funnels. Fills bottle and squeezes water out—fills again—puts bottle in mouth watching theatre
9.50 a.m. orderly out of the corner of her eye. Puts doll in
9.55 a.m. water—baths doll 'I washing my doll'. Washes doll's hair—squeezes cloth, wets again—turns doll over and sits her in bowl—washes doll and chats to sister. Stands doll up in water—bends doll's legs —reaches in locker and gets soap—soaps cloth—
10.00 a.m. washes doll's face—wraps soap in face-cloth—smiles at sister—tells what she is doing—turns doll upside down—washes doll's hair—wearing contented 'maternal' look. Squeezes cloth—puts cloth
10.05 a.m. and soap on locker. Sister comes and washes her face—dries own face. Sister encourages her to dry doll—chats happily to sister—makes soapy water —plays with plastic bottle. Sings—smiles—washes

F

doll's hair—reaches for rubber toy from locker and puts in water—washes rubber toy. Busily
10.10 a.m. squeezes cloth and watches soapy water dropping into bowl—back to washing doll with great
10.15 a.m. vigour. Wipes locker top with cloth, lips seriously set and purposeful, dries locker—squeezes out cloth. Makes a great deal of lather—washes doll—
10.20 a.m. Teacher comes—chats—removes apron, stands at end of bed jigging and singing. Teacher encourages her to clear up—helps put all containers, cloths, etc. in bowl—climbs around happily on
10.25 a.m. bed chatting all the time.

Carl, aged three and a half years, was receiving treatment for spina bifida and dislocation of the hips. He had frequent readmissions to hospital and had been in for ten days this time. He was in a cot with a swinging cot-tray in front of him.

The teacher gave Carl a toy farm, and, on request, a 'dinky' bus, saying 'Is this the one your mum comes on?' to which Carl replied, 'Yes, she'll be here in a minute.' There followed some conversation about mother and visiting. After this Carl played with the farm for ten minutes, then asked to do painting. He painted for fifteen minutes, experimenting also with the unspillable water-pot. Next he chose doll-bathing, and proceeded to bath the doll with great vigour, giving a running commentary—'Wash her bottom, wash her legs, wash her hands—etc.' He spent ten minutes washing the doll and experimenting with soap and water. Throughout this session Carl talked to nurses, orderlies, the mother of another child and the teacher.

Children's long-stay hospital (H)
The country branch of a children's hospital, where the bun-

galow-style wards are scattered over extensive grounds. They were light, bright and airy, open along one side and with a solarium on to which the beds were pushed in good weather. The day on which this observation was made was warm and sunny and all the cots and beds were outside. There was free visiting, but as the hospital was out in the country mothers could not always visit daily. There was a full-time school where trained nursery teachers were employed for the under-fives, in addition to nursery nurses employed by the hospital. Great thought was given to the children's play needs and many of the usual nursery-school occupations, such as sand, water and dough were in evidence.

Heather, aged three years, had been in hospital for two years with congenitally dislocated hips. Heather had a poor home background and showed signs of ill-tratment on admission. She was rarely visited. At the time of observation both hips were in plaster, but she was allowed the maximum mobility by being placed on her stomach on a special trolley on castors which she could propel around the floor by using her hands (gloved) as paddles. At the beginning of the observation she had a large sand-try on the floor in front of her.

10.10 a.m. Making patterns in the sand with her fingers. Sieving sand through a plastic seive. Squeezing sand through her fingers. Filling a plastic bucket and turning out shapes. Teacher comes with a fur-
10.15 a.m. ther selection of sand toys and Heather chooses several. Pats sand into small moulds and turns it
10.20 a.m. out. Scoops up sand and buries sieve—repeats this
10.25 a.m. operation several times. Builds up heaps of sand and knocks them over. Scoops up sand and trickles it through outstretched fingers. Squeezes sand in between hands. Fills funnel and allows sand to

83

10.30 a.m.	trickle through into a heap. Leans chin on hand and
10.35 a.m.	gazes around. Teacher comes and brushes sand off her hands and puts her gloves on so that she can push the trolley round during the lunch break.
10.40–11.00 a.m.	Lunch break.
11.05 a.m.	Teacher gives bowl of water, sponge, soap, plastic bottle, towel and doll. Spends some time squeez-
11.10 a.m.	ing water through sponge with obvious enjoyment. Soaps sponge and scrubs doll vigorously. Squeezes water from plastic bottle on to doll.
11.15 a.m.	Continues washing doll. Dances doll up and down in the water. Dabbles her own fingers in the water. Teacher gives her more soap and suggests that she makes the water really soapy for blowing
11.20 a.m.	bubbles. Vigorously rubbing soap in hands, telling Observer that she is going to blow bubbles. Teacher brings bubble-pipe and Heather blows large bubbles, laughing gleefully. Dabbles her hands in the foamy water. Blows with renewed
11.25 a.m.	vigour and bursts the bubbles as they rise, laughing delightedly. Puts doll back into the bubbly
11.30 a.m.	water, covering her with foam.

Jonathan, *aged twenty-three months*, had club feet and had been in hospital for three weeks. His mother visited fairly often. He had a swinging cot-tray on which were bricks, a doll, a cradle, a teddy bear and a cardboard box. His face wore the lost, slightly puzzled air, of the toddler who finds himself in hospital.

10.10 a.m.	Fixes bricks together. Loves doll. Puts bricks in cradle. Calls out 'Plane!' and points 'talking' to teacher about it. Piles bricks on upturned box, singing 'Oh Dolly, Oh Dolly'. Examines doll and
10.20 a.m.	puts it in the cradle—tips cradle and shows doll in

84

it to little girl in the next cot. Piles bricks up and
10.25 a.m. knocks them down, making a good deal of noise.
Points to toy-trolley and asks teacher for some-
10.30 a.m. thing (unintelligible). Given nesting toy. Packs
bricks away in box with teacher's help and dis-
covers how to open nesting toy, with pleased ex-
10.35 a.m. clamation at finding another doll inside. Goes on
exploring nesting toy, trying to fit it together
again. Tires of this and demands something else
but teacher explains that it is lunch time.

Lunch break

11.05 a.m. Has been given doll, bath, sponge, soap, water
and towel and thoroughly enjoys dabbling in the
water, busily squeezing the sponge and rubbing
11.10 a.m. the doll. Experiments with squeezing sponge and
dropping it back in the water. Sucks sponge.
Stands doll up in bath and washes its face. Fills
sponge with water and squeezes it on to his own
11.15 a.m. hair. Drops sponge back into water—sucks it. Ex-
11.20 a.m. periments with sponge in and out of water. Puts
11.25 a.m. doll in bath, takes it out and throws it over side of
cot looking expectantly at teacher, who does not
see. 'Washes' his own hair with the wet sponge.
Teacher sees and comes to mop up—drying hair
and mopping up spills on plastic sheet covering
11.30 a.m. bed. Jonathan enjoys the fun.

Nicola, aged three and a half years, who had dislocated hips, was
a very chatty little girl. She had a book and a doll on her bed.
There was a bowl of sand and various sand toys on her cot-
tray. She played with this for twenty minutes, pouring it from
one container to another, making pies, and rubbing her hands
in it gleefully, saying, 'Look, I'm going to make all dirt—I'm

85

doing it with my hands'. Later she played with a teaset and water for twenty minutes, pouring out tea and offering it to the teacher and the nurses.

Teaching Hospital (*J*)

The children's ward in a large London teaching hospital, which although old-fashioned and inconveniently arranged, had a happy permissive atmosphere. Daily visiting, morning, afternoon and evening, was allowed and mothers were encouraged to do as much as possible for their children. There was an established school and children of the two to five age group were included. Nursery nurses were employed but play was not considered part of their duties. There was good liaison between school and hospital, and the ward sister, very much aware of the problems of children in hospital, appreciated the value of keeping the children happily occupied.

Lorraine, aged three and a half years, was readmitted the previous day for investigation because of fits. She has previously been in hospital for seven days at the age of two and a half years. One side of her cot was down, but she had restrainers on. On her bed were a teddy, a soft toy and a Noah's Ark. She was pale and a little 'lost' looking.

10.25 a.m. Looking through partition by her bed in an expressionless, uninterested way. Lifts roof of Noah's Ark, takes out an animal, plays with it without apparently paying attention to it. Looks all around her, takes roof off Noah's Ark, peers through door, picks up giraffe and swings it back and forth, plays 'peep-bo' through door, stands animals up on the deck, examining them one by one, but

10.30 a.m. looking around her at intervals. Kneels up to look through partition at nurse, still with same lack of expression—lies down and rubs head, sits up and looks round, watches orderly changing towels,

10.35 a.m. plays with animals in the ark—stands up hanging on to cot side looking rather wistfully through partition, lolls back into corner of cot lethargically playing with hair-ribbon, biting it and putting it round her neck, always with eyes questing round the ward—coughs, hangs out of bed—turns back

10.40 a.m. to Noah's Ark—talks to orderly—starts to cry— orderly comforts her and talks about animals— stands animals on deck of ark in rather desultory way then suddenly sweeps them off impatiently. Puts animals back in ark, looking rather bored and

10.45 a.m. a little sad—lies back in corner of cot and rubs head—plays with hair-ribbon—picks up giraffe and drops it from arm's length to cot—looks through partition, tugging at cot side. Teacher approaches. 'I want some other toys'. 'Would you like a doll's house?' 'Yes'. Puts animals away in

10.50 a.m. ark and teacher brings doll's house—becomes absorbed in moving and arranging furniture. House surgeon approaches—makes immediate happy contact. 'I'm all right'. House surgeon: 'Would

10.55 a.m. you like to go home?' Brightens and nods emphatically. Continues playing with doll's house, talks to staff nurse about it. Staff nurse stays and

11.00 a.m. plays with her for a few seconds—chats happily to staff nurse. Needs toiletting—chats to staff nurse all the time—back to arranging doll's house smil-

11.10 a.m. ing and talking to herself. Nurse takes older new girl to see her, talking and naming objects in doll's

11.15 a.m. house. Nurse departs. Lorraine takes out bed and doll and becomes very absorbed in making the

87

11.20 a.m.   bed and putting the doll in it. Interest beginning to diminish—lies waving legs and chewing hairribbon. Pathologist approaches to do blood-

11.25 a.m.   test. 'I don't want that—I don't like it'. Pathologist tries to reassure her but she continues to cry and struggle. Young nurse comes and holds her, speaking calmly. Stays some time afterwards comforting her very nicely until she gradually calms down saying 'I don't like that doctor. I like my doctor'.

Discussion of findings

In these observations the children themselves demonstrate their needs very clearly. The way in which some of these needs appear to have been met is also evident in many cases.

STABLE RELATIONSHIP

First and foremost was the need for a stable relationship. Eileen in hospital L, p. 60, Kevin in D, p. 37, and William in M, p. 62, who were all children whose mothers rarely visited, showed this need very clearly. Eileen (four years old), p. 60, in hospital for over twenty months, must have had innumerable mothers of other children attempting to fulfil her play needs. She appeared to be unable to play with any degree of concentration with the attractive toys with which she was provided, her time and attention being entirely taken up with the need to persuade someone to come to talk to her or to play with her. She demonstrated, too, the touch hunger of the deprived child. Kevin (four years old), p. 37, also demonstrated, albeit much more overtly, the insistent demanding of the institutionalized child. William (three years old), p. 62, who was restless and mischievous, was said to be impervious to admonition of any kind. In the course of one hour many people scolded, loved, prohibited and laughed at him; small wonder that he gave heed to no one. The other children's mothers who supervised the play in this ward were kind to him but were so concerned with protecting their own children's possessions from his marauding hands that they were unable to give him the kind of attention and understanding that he was obviously needing or to provide his natural drive towards exploration and learning with a legitimate outlet.

Compare these children with Heather (three years old), p. 83, two years in H, rarely visited by her mother, who settled happily for comparatively long periods to sand and water play in a ward where continuous relationships and consistent handling are provided by a nursery teacher and nursery nurses. Just as the child at home will play contentedly knowing that his mother is at hand, so the child in hospital is able to concentrate on his play when he is assured of 'on demand' attention.

It was evident that the establishment of a continuous relationship contributed towards helping children to accept hospital procedures. It was most marked that in hospitals where there was no one person responsible for the provision of play the children rarely asked staff for reassurance, whereas in hospitals where 'on demand' attention was available children were able to signify their needs. When distressed by watching another child have a blood-test in K hospital, Marie (three and a half years old), p. 76, called for the play lady. Juliet (four years old), p. 75, it is interesting to note, asked for painting immediately afterwards, becoming completely absorbed when given it, though she had obviously been very much disturbed by the incident. Garry (five years old), p. 41, in D, who had no one he was able to ask for an occupation, showed his tension and anxiety by chewing his pyjama sleeve. It is interesting to note that he was unable to eat his dinner when it was served.

That security in relationship can help children to accept hospitalization is demonstrated by Marie in K, p. 76. The play leader reported that Marie always returns to hospital knowing exactly which toys she is going to play with and on the day of observation she was demanding the story that she had obviously come to regard as suitable post-operative treatment, settling down contentedly to sleep afterwards. Compare this child with Tracey (four years old), p. 73, in O, also seen on the day following her operation, without toys, looking pale and bored, fiddling with a paper bag on her locker and gazing longingly through the partition at other children playing.

The paramount importance of the personality of the play supervisor is shown in F, p. 43, where the elderly teacher employed for the over-fives had a fascinating 'Pied Piper' quality which made all the children, even the toddlers, gather round her, regardless of the fact that the story she was reading was intended for older children and that she had no exciting toys to give them. It seems that even in a hospital where admissions and discharges are frequent, a tradition of security can grow up round a particular person.

SOMEONE WITH TIME TO ASSESS THEIR NEEDS

Unless there is someone with sufficient time to observe them carefully, and with sufficient knowledge and experience to assess their needs, many signs of disturbance will remain unnoticed, and many opportunities for helping the children will be missed. If there is no one specifically to watch over their psychological well-being many children most in need of help will be overlooked. Sally (five years old) in P, p. 47, and Sandra in D, p. 39, two quiet, 'very good', withdrawn children, were virtually ignored. It is interesting to note that

Sandra burst into tears when somebody eventually did go near her. What state of mind was induced in the two-year-old isolated, without toys, in a bare single side ward in N hospital, p. 45? The teacher in G was able to provide Wendy (three years, ten months old), p. 81, with the means of working out a specific difficulty in water play, and by her discussion of home and mother with Helen (three years old), p. 79, helped to release her from her tension so that she was able to become absorbed in her play.

If the teacher in S had had time to observe Stephen (four years old), p. 53, more closely she would probably have realized that his distress arose from his dislike of keeping his possessions in the hospital locker; provision of something in which to pack them might well have relieved this distress. Gloria (three years old), p. 55, in T, might have been helped through the desolation of being the only child in the ward without a visitor. (It is interesting to note here that at the end of the session she was too upset to take notice of the nurse who went to speak to her.) Martin (one and a half years old), p. 46, in N, showing his disturbance by plucking and eating the fur from his teddy bear, Karen (one year, seven months old), p. 71, in B, eating paper from the highly unsuitable football annual set in front of her, and Anthony (one year, eleven months old), p. 37, in A, holding his shoe and staring into space, all seemed to be in need of help. Certainly Jonathan (one year, eleven months old), p. 84, in H, seemed to benefit from having the attention of an adult who took time and trouble to find a satisfying occupation for him. This observation of Jonathan does seem to indicate that at least temporary relief from separation anxiety can be given to the two-year-old in hospital. Maybe we should not accept too readily the idea that if mother is not present there is little that can be done for these younger children.

Play facilities in children's wards

On a more practical level, Kevin (two years old), p. 45, shows how the provision of a suitable table can bring life and vigour to a child's play, though in this particular instance it was supplied inadvertently.

INTEREST AND ENCOURAGEMENT

In the hospital situation where there is much that is disturbing and distracting, children need more than ever to be given the interest and encouragement of an adult if their play is to be at all beneficial. Jane (three years old) in B, p. 70, became interested in the materials provided only when the nursery nurse in charge talked with her about them for a few minutes, most of the rest of the hour being spent in restless head-rolling and fidgetting. Stephen (three years, one month old) in O, p. 74, only took an apathetic interest in his books and toys but smiled and responded instantly when a nurse played with him. Rupert (five years old) in R, p. 67, ignoring his books and puzzles, rolled restlessly on his bed, but appeared very pleased and interested when Observer talked to him about them at the end of the observation. John (three years, seven months old) in P, p. 48, who played rather restlessly and aimlessly with several small toys, concentrated on his puzzle when encouraged by a staff nurse and William (three years old) in M, p. 63, showed his longest period of concentration (four minutes) when another child's mother showed an interest in his manipulation of the Jack in the Box. Carl (three and a half years old) in G, p. 82, also had several changes of occupation but played with a much greater air of purpose and concentration than either John or William and frequently called on the teacher to admire what he was doing or to help him. It was most marked in hospital K, p. 74, where much of the play material was somewhat limited and unstimulating, that children played in a much more settled fashion when someone was there 'on demand' to help and admire.

Susan (three years old) in R, p. 68, showing the 'scatter-brain' play of the disturbed child, and Garry (three and a half years old) in E, p. 41, restlessly wandering, appeared to need direction and encouragement. Fanny (four years, seven months old), p. 78, also a disturbed child, was restless at the beginning of the observation but settled down for twenty minutes to pasting pictures when encouraged by the teacher and later joined a group listening to a story.

On the whole the children who could run about were better able to entertain themselves but even their play was apt to be rather desultory without someone to take an interest in it, as Julie (two years, one month old), p. 35, shows.

COMMUNICATION

It was noticeable that where children were happily occupied with interesting play material more people went to speak to them. This is readily understood for it is much easier to make contact with an alert, interested child than with one who is bored and apathetic. There is a noteworthy discrepancy between the numbers of social (as opposed to nursing) contacts made by children in hospitals with play facilities and those with none at all. In the former there was an average of five contacts in the course of an hour, while in the latter there was only ·75. Lorraine in J, p. 86, and Carl in G, p. 82, both showed how interesting materials lead to conversation. The observation on Carl also shows how the skilful teacher uses every opportunity to bring mother nearer, in this case by her seemingly casual introduction of the bus, saying 'Is this the one your mum comes in?'.

The extremes of disturbance and frustration caused by inability to communicate are demonstrated by Connie, the little

Cypriot girl in M, p. 64. Connie's behaviour is an interesting example of alternating aggression and withdrawal, the latter taking the form of curling up into a ball in the corner of her cot. It was obvious here that the mothers supervising play were so disconcerted by this behaviour that they left her severely alone. Thus she was ignored for the very reasons that she needed help.

It seemed that where there was someone to give full-time attention to their needs, children played in a much more settled fashion. This is shown quite dramatically when the one-hour time samples of eight pairs of children of similar age and length of stay in hospital are compared. Children in wards with supervised play show a total average of 39·4 minutes of settled play (17·4 minutes with any one occupation), whereas those in wards with no play supervisor show a total average of 3·8 minutes (4·9 minutes with any one occupation). The latter was almost invariably set off by adult attention, as the following diagrams show.

SUITABLE MATERIALS

While the personality and presence of the play leader are of paramount importance, as has already been pointed out, stimulating material may contribute largely to the promotion of settled play and the relief of tension and anxiety. Helen (three years old) in G, p. 79, who appeared to be tense and anxious, played with sand for twenty-five minutes, becoming completely absorbed in it for at least fifteen minutes of that time and again showed great absorption in dressing and undressing the teddy bears. Jonathan (one year, eleven months old) in H, p. 84, played for twenty minutes with soap and water. Compare these two children with John (three years, seven months old) in P, p. 48, who played in a rather restless, aimless manner

Time samples showing the play of children of comparable age and length of stay in hospital

A

H. Heather (three years old)
2 years in hospital

B

L. Eileen (four years old)
23 months in hospital

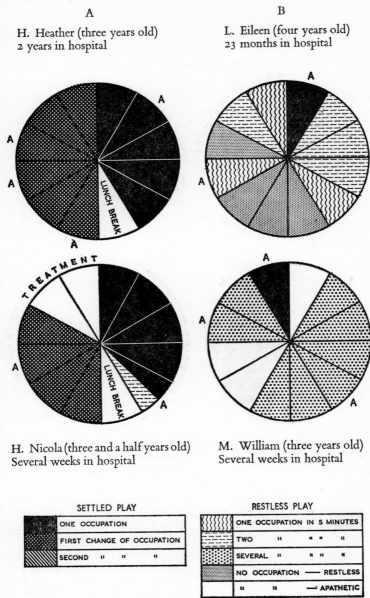

H. Nicola (three and a half years old)
Several weeks in hospital

M. William (three years old)
Several weeks in hospital

SETTLED PLAY

	ONE OCCUPATION
	FIRST CHANGE OF OCCUPATION
	SECOND " " "

RESTLESS PLAY

	ONE OCCUPATION IN 5 MINUTES
	TWO " " " "
	SEVERAL " " " "
	NO OCCUPATION —— RESTLESS
	" " —— APATHETIC

A A A   Adult gives attention to play
N.B.—'occupation' signifies anything occupying the attention.

Time samples showing the play of children of comparable age and length of stay in hospital

A   B

G. Helen (three years old)   O. Stephen (three years and one
9 days in hospital   month
                                                       21 days in hospital

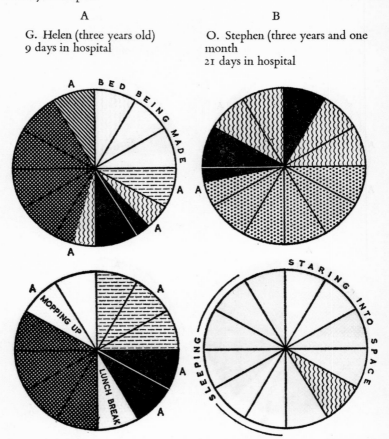

H. Jonathan (one year and eleven   A. Anthony (one year and eleven
months)   months)
3 weeks in hospital   2 weeks in hospital

	SETTLED PLAY
	ONE OCCUPATION
	FIRST CHANGE OF OCCUPATION
	SECOND · " " "

	RESTLESS PLAY
	ONE OCCUPATION IN 5 MINUTES
	TWO " " · "
	SEVERAL " " " "
	NO OCCUPATION —— RESTLESS
	" " —— APATHETIC

A A A   Adult gives attention to play
N.B.—'occupation' signifies anything occupying the attention.

Time samples showing the play of children of comparable age and length of stay in hospital

A
G. Carl (three and a half years old)
10 days in hospital

B
P. John (three years, seven months)
3 weeks in hospital

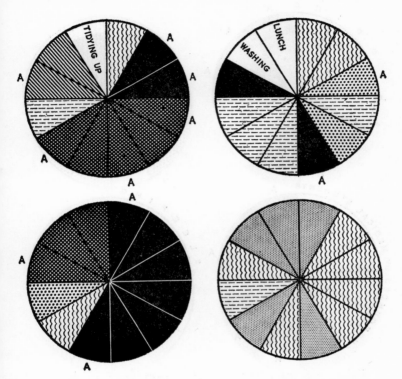

K. Juliet (four years old)
14 days in hospital

D. Garry (five years old)
18 days in hospital

SETTLED PLAY	
ONE OCCUPATION	
FIRST CHANGE OF OCCUPATION	
SECOND " " "	

RESTLESS PLAY	
ONE OCCUPATION IN 5 MINUTES	
TWO " " " "	
SEVERAL " " " "	
NO OCCUPATION —— RESTLESS	
" " —— APATHETIC	

A A A   Adult gives attention to play
N.B.—'occupation' signifies anything occupying the attention.

Time samples showing the play of children of comparable age and length of stay in hospital

A	B
K. Marie (three and a half years old) 3 days in hospital	T. Gloria (three years old) 2 days in hospital

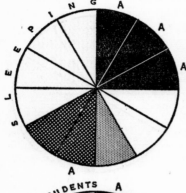 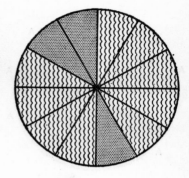

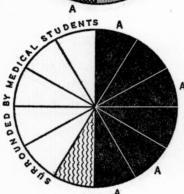 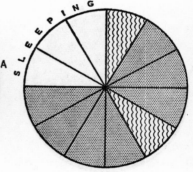

C. William (four years, three months) 2 days in hospital	O. Tracey (four years old) 2 days in hospital

SETTLED PLAY		RESTLESS PLAY	
ONE OCCUPATION		ONE OCCUPATION IN 5 MINUTES	
FIRST CHANGE OF OCCUPATION		TWO " " " "	
SECOND " " " "		SEVERAL " " " "	
		NO OCCUPATION —— RESTLESS	
		" " —— APATHETIC	

N.B.—Marie, Gloria, and Tracey were post-operative cases.
      William had had a minor accident.
A A A Adult gives attention to play
N.B.—'occupation' signifies anything occupying the attention.

with a number of unstimulating toys, and Julie (two years, one month old) in A, p. 35, who was given a naked doll with which to play or told to go shopping (with nothing!). Neither of these children played for more than five minutes with any one toy.

Wendy (three years, ten months old) in G, p. 81, and Heather (three years old) in H, p. 83, were both children who had shown signs of ill-treatment and disturbance on admission to hospital. Both showed themselves able to become absorbed in their play, Wendy with water for thirty-five minutes and Heather first with sand for twenty-five minutes and then water for twenty-five minutes.

William (four years, three months old) in C, p. 77, found relief in playing with a 'safe' toy, a construction set which he hailed gleefully as being like the one he had at home.

Garry (five years old) in D, p. 38, Mason (four years old), p. 50, and David (three years old), p. 51, in Q, had nothing exciting to play with and presented a picture of restless boredom. Mason and David particularly illustrate the sad predicament of lively small boys admitted to hospital feeling quite well, put into bed for (to them) no apparent reason, admonished when their natural liveliness momentarily rises above their bewilderment in this strange situation, awaiting an operation in a state of mounting tension and anxiety as the minutes tick slowly by.

The satisfaction derived from messy play is demonstrated by Nicola (three years, six months old) in H, p. 85, joyously announcing 'I'm going to make all dirt' as she rubbed her hands in the sand. Carl (three years, six months old) in G, p. 82, delighted in splashing water and paint, and Jonathan (one year, eleven months old) in H, p. 84, happily dabbled his hands in soapy water. Compare these children with Gloria (three years old) in T, p. 55, in an excessively clean and tidy ward, tucked up tidily in a clean bed with a naked plastic doll, reduced to washing it with 'spit'.

LEGITIMATE OUTLET FOR AGGRESSION

Hospitalization and separation from mother will amost inevitably arouse hostile feelings in the child. This is demonstrated clearly by Laura's treatment of the doll her mother brought her, in the film *The Two-Year-Old Goes to Hospital*. The accompanying observations also show several children behaving aggressively towards their dolls and teddy bears. Mason (four years old) in Q, p. 50, treated his doll and teddy bear very roughly, finally rejecting them altogether, and David (three years old), p. 51, alternately loved and ill-treated his teddy, showing his inner conflict in the ambivalence of his feelings towards it. Gloria (three years old) in T, p. 55, beat her doll and manhandled it quite severely. None of these children had any means of constructive or 'reparative' play, such as putting the doll or teddy to bed or bandaging it. This process of 'taking it out' on a well-loved toy or one which mother has specially brought in may well leave the child with strong feelings of unresolved guilt.

The building up and destruction of sand heaps demonstrated by Heather (three years old) in H, p. 83, shows a much more satisfactory way of dealing with aggression and one which is not likely to leave the child with feelings of guilt about having destroyed a beloved object.

SATISFACTORY MEANS OF EXPLORATION AND EXPERIMENT

Apart from promoting comparatively long periods of concentration a variety of stimulating material provides children with opportunities for learning through exploration and experiment. Helen, Heather, Nicola, Carl and Jonathan all showed themselves to be exploring the nature of the materials they were handling and to be experimenting with them in a variety of ways. Julie (two years, one month old) in A, p. 35, at the 'into everything' stage of development, had no exciting material to explore and so spent her time wandering aimlessly. Similarly John (three years, seven months old) in P, p. 48, could only experiment in a very limited way with his small plastic toys, using, with commendable ingenuity, the tumbler provided for orange juice. William (three years old) in M, p. 62, for several weeks, obviously suffered from lack of legitimate means of using his drive to explore and find out. Eileen (four years old) in L hospital, p. 60, had also missed many months of opportunity for learning owing to the haphazard method of issuing play material and lack of adult attention.

GENERAL POINTS OF INTEREST

Several other points of interest emerge from these observations. Ian (three years, six months old) in I, p. 58, shows by his reaction when his mother arrived to take him home that a child may conceal his anxiety in apparently settled play. In the same hospital the observation of Neil (three years old), p. 58, indicates that the presence of mother does not always produce settled play. On the other hand Douglas (five years old) in E, p. 40, only began to play with any degree of interest when his mother arrived.

That the removal of school-age children or even teaching them on the ward may further deprive the under-fives of a source of comfort or attention is shown by Stephen in S, p. 53, who cheered up considerably when the boy next to him was released from lessons and able to talk to him. William (four years, three months old) in C, p. 77, visibly regressed in his play and his behaviour when put under the strain of being examined by several medical students. It could well be that the apparently aimless wandering of several of the children, for example Garry (three years, six months old) in E, p. 41, and William (three years old) in M, p. 62, is a similar form of regression under strain, a regression to the two-year-old stage of rapid shifts in attention.

SUMMING UP

Of the fifty children observed, sixteen played in a restless, aimless manner, probably due to lack of a relationship with an interested adult and unstimulating play material; three were withdrawn; seven showed some evidence of disturbance, such as head-rolling, nose-picking, hair-pulling or eating foreign substances; two had no toys at all; nine showed purposeful play and seemed to benefit from it; nine seemed to benefit from the presence of a play supervisor even though the material used did not appear to be very stimulating; four had their mothers present, which quite naturally influenced their play.

Assessment of provisions made

Children's hospitals generally had plenty of toys but these were not well looked after or suitably distributed unless there was a play leader in charge. It is remarkable that four out of six children's hospitals (excluding the long-stay) had not made any provision for supervising play. It may be that the assumption is that paediatric trained nurses will do this automatically but there was little evidence of this. Indeed the nurses in most of the wards were too busy to pay more than passing attention to the children.

In teaching hospitals there was evidence of more awareness of the need for attention to play, though the quality of the actual provision made varied considerably. Three out of five relied on casual supervision of mothers of in-patients. There were usually plenty of toys.

General hospitals were on the whole less well provided and showed little evidence of thought being given to occupying the children.

Many hospitals had well-stocked playrooms which were not being fully used owing to lack of staff for supervision.

NURSERY TEACHERS

Of the provisions made, nursery play within the established hospital schools (under local Education Authorities) appeared to be most satisfactory. Here the children were being given normal nursery school activities together with the attention of a trained teacher and the observations would seem to indicate that they were deriving benefit from this. The drawback to this kind of arrangement is that teachers work school hours, therefore there may be periods in the evenings and during week-ends and school holidays for which no provision is made. Some schools do make provision for the long summer holiday.

PLAY LEADERS

In the one hospital visited where a 'play therapist', who was a trained nursery nurse, was employed, the children were again most successfully occupied, though some of the play material here was less stimulating. The 'on demand' provision of adult attention seemed to help the children to become absorbed in their play.

In both of the above situations it was obvious that nursing staff took more interest in the children's play than in those hospitals where no provision was made.

Play facilities in children's wards

NURSERY NURSES

The observations showed that nursery nurses employed for general child-care duties did not in fact give sufficient time or attention to the children's play needs. This might well be because too much was expected of them in the way of general duties or that they themselves were not sufficiently aware of children's great psychological need of play. Many of them too were very young and would probably have been better with the support of an experienced supervisor.

MOTHERS OF IN-PATIENTS

Of all the methods of attempting to deal with the supervision of play that of leaving it to mothers of children in the wards was least satisfactory. These mothers, who quite naturally were primarily concerned with the well-being of their own children and insufficiently secure themselves in the hospital situation, lacked the necessary breadth of experience in dealing with all types of children and therefore the insight necessary to the assessment of their specific needs and difficulties; e.g. reaction to anxiety and frustration by showing either extreme aggression or complete withdrawal. Added to this, a child hospitalized for a long period, whose own mother was unable to visit frequently, had to deal with a succession of strangers. It should however be noted here that in the hospitals where play was mother-supervised there was invariably an abundance of toys in evidence.

TEACHERS FOR SCHOOL-AGE CHILDREN

In hospitals where the Local Education Authority supplied teachers for children over five, many of them gave an eye to the younger ones when they had time, but this was a very haphazard method and depended solely on the interest and goodwill of the teachers concerned.

NO SPECIAL PROVISION

Of the hospitals where no special provision was made, two had a happy permissive atmosphere and plenty of toys in evidence but the children's play lacked the air of purpose and absorption shown when an adult is on the spot expressly to stimulate and take an interest; four had a fair number of toys in evidence but these were distributed indiscriminately and no one attempted to stimulate play; three were extremely tidy, highly polished and had no toys in evidence apart from each child's personal possessions, mainly soft toys or plastic animals. It was in these seven latter that the most obvious signs of disturbance were noted.

3 - Doll-play projective test

N.B.—This test can only be regarded as a pilot scheme. It is included here because there is a strong indication that the doll-play projective technique could be a valuable source of information about children in hospital.

Reasons for selection

Close observation of the free behaviour of children at play, methods used by Piaget and Susan Isaacs among others, show very clearly their reactions to the situations in which they may find themselves and the problems confronting them. In *Imagination in Early Childhood* Ruth Griffiths describes the use of projective tests in revealing the areas of emotional conflict in children. Doll-play, a projective technique largely developed in America, gives insight into a more specific area of children's problems. Piaget[1] says that we may be sure that all the happenings, pleasant or unpleasant, in the child's life will have repercussions on her dolls. In a monograph on *Young Children's Play Fantasies* Geo Bach[2] states that doll-play is 'a sensitive indicator of psychological changes brought about by changes in the social environment of the child'. Beulah Winstell, Elizabeth Robinson and Margaret Pintler have all

---

[1] Piaget, *Play, Dreams and Imagination.*
[2] Geo Bach, *Young Children's play Fantasies.*

demonstrated the value of this technique in revealing the effects of early life circumstances, the child's attitude towards his world and the people in it and the areas in which his main problems lie. This then would seem to be an appropriate method to use in attempting to discover the effects of hospitalization on young children and whether in fact the provision of adequate play facilities has any moderating influence.

The children selected

The first intention had been to use the test with children in hospital but on reflection it was thought that a better indication of their attitude to hospitalization might be given when the immediate memory had faded. For purposes of convenience and as time available for the study was limited, children seven years and under in the nursery and infant classes of day schools for the physically handicapped were selected. As the selection was limited to children who had been in hospital between the ages of two and five years, it soon became evident that satisfactory pairing was impossible and it was decided to test as many children of average intelligence as fulfilled this one requirement, grouping them according to whether they had been in hospitals with adequate play facilities or those where no provision is made. Spastic children were eliminated because of motor and speech difficulties. In all, fifteen children were tested, but for purposes of comparison only ten of these were selected for analysis.

The structure of the test and method of presentation

Ruth Phillips,[1] a member of a team at the Iowa Child Welfare Research Station under the direction of Dr. Robert Sears,

[1] Ruth Phillips, *Doll-play as a function of the Realism of the Materials & the Length of the Experimental Session.*

investigated the type of play materials most suitable. She used both 'low realism materials', i.e. featureless dolls and blocks, and 'high realism' materials and found that the latter made for more exploratory and less organizational behaviour. She also found that short and frequent play sessions were best. Elizabeth Robinson[2] found that a duplicate family caused greater identification. The greater part of the work on the doll-play projective technique has been done using the family and home situation, but here it was decided to use a hospital situation with high realism material, in order to make an immediate impact on the child's memory of hospital.

The material used, although realistic, was not too detailed lest interest in detail should inhibit fantasy. The dolls represented a doctor, a sister, a nurse, mother and father, two babies, one small boy and girl and one larger boy and girl, the

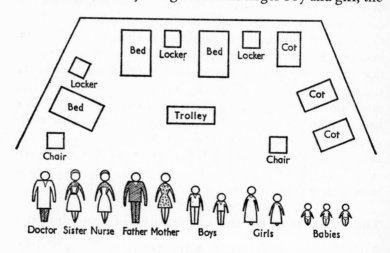

Diagram of layout of 'ward'

[2] Elizabeth Robinson in *Doll play as a Function of the Doll Family Constellation*.

children all being dressed either in pyjamas or nightdresses.

The furniture was set out (as shown in the diagram) at the beginning of each session and the dolls were laid out in a row in front of it. At the beginning of the first session the following introduction was made: 'This is a children's hospital and here are the children who go in it. This is the doctor, nurse, etc. You may play with it just as you wish. I am going to do my work while you play.' No further comment was made unless the child asked a question or seemed to need encouragement. Occasionally a question was asked, for example 'Is the baby crying?' 'Who will comfort it?' 'What is he doing?' but on the whole these were found to have an inhibiting effect on the play and were only used when the situation seemed to demand it.

The tester made the acquaintance of the children beforehand and invited them to come and play with some special toys in another room. Because children in schools for the physically handicapped are accustomed to being taken out of their class for treatment and medicals, this was accepted as a matter of course and no child showed any apprehension at being led away. These children are also used to making contact with many people, therefore the establishment of a relationship with the tester was made easy. The tester aimed at providing a reassuring and secure background without in any way influencing or stimulating the children. Four twenty-minute sessions were given to each child.

METHOD OF RECORDING AND ANALYSIS

Recording, which was done as unobtrusively as possible, presented some difficulty. As some children were heavily handicapped and needed help it was found impossible to use the more satisfactory time-sample method, so the assessments were made on each completed action or theme. The number of actions assigned to each category are expressed as a percentage of the total number of actions for each child, since there was a good deal of variation in the number of actions. Where the child withdrew completely from the material, not returning to it during that session, his total number of actions is calculated on a basis of the average number for children with complete sessions, the balance being counted as tangential actions.

CODE USED IN ANALYSIS OF DOLL-PLAY

The categories used are adaptations of those used in previous studies.

E.   *Exploratory*. Any activity familiarizing the subject with the material, i.e. examination of furniture, clothing, comments on hair, or such questions as 'Does this come off?' 'Will this undo?'.

O.   *Organizational*. All purposeful arrangement of materials, reorganization, naming or counting.

Th.   *Thematic*. Any doll action or verbalization suitable to time, place, situation and characters involved.

I. Th. *Individualized Thematic*. Actions indicating an element of inappropriateness to the theme in which materials are not being used according to their given purpose, but which seem to indicate some personal reaction.

I.   *Identification*. Activity or verbalization in which the child relates himself to the theme (hospital) or materials.

T.   *Tangential*. Withdrawal or diversion from the materials.

TX.   Random manipulation of the materials.

       Aggression

A−   Verbal aggression or threat, not carried out, e.g. 'I'll smack you'. Implied aggression, e.g. smiling when someone falls.

A   Hostility expressed verbally or in action to dolls, equipment or observer or from dolls to each other or to equipment.

A+ Excessive hostility expressed vehemently or in pro-longed violent action.

The analysis of the actions presented many difficulties. For example, it was not always apparent whether certain actions were organizational or thematic and the tester was obliged to fall back on her memory of the 'climate' of the child's play in making her decision. This method was also used in assessing acts of aggression. It is not easy to convey in written records that 'quality and intensity of affect expressed during the play' which Beulah Winstel[1] considers of great importance. For this particular test the term 'Individualized thematic' was applied to any action which would not normally take place in a children's ward but which definitely appeared to be a part of the child's hospital theme. Such actions as piling lockers and standing people on top, putting the adults in beds and cots, tipping the children out of bed or wheeling the trolley over them were assigned to this category. 'Identification' was applied to any action or verbalization either direct or implied, in which the child related himself to the hospital whether in present play or recall of past events, but direct references to home or family, unless connected with hospital were treated as 'tangential', e.g. Anna Maria's stories of conflict between mother and father and Stephen C's references to his father's appearance and his job.

Detailed reports of doll-play

A summary of each child's four sessions is included here, together with one or two extracts from each detailed record.

[1] Beulah Winstell in *Use of Controlled Doll-Play Situation in Determining Certain Effects of Maternal Attitudes on Children.*

Doll-play projective test

	Name	Age	Position in family	Home	Intelligence	Age at hospit zati
A.	Edward	7	1/1	good	average	4
A.	Anne	4.11	4/5	poor	average	2.6
A+	Sarah	6.5	4/6	good	average	3
A.	Ronnie	5	2/2	good	average	1
A+	Norman	6	1/1	good	above average	2.0
B.	David	5	2/2	good	average	2
B.	Joseph	4.6	2/5	fair	average	8 mor
B.	John	4	1/1	good	not assessed	2
B.	Mary	5	1/1	good	average	2
B.	James	5.9	2/2	f. good	average	4.

N.B. *Home rating* on Health Visitor's or Teacher's repor
Play Provision rating A+ Good, if full-time.

LECTED

Length of stay	Age at last hospitali-zation	Length of stay	No. of times	Play provision
-4 weeks	6.7	4 weeks	2	fair
veral weeks	3.10	several weeks	6	fair
veral months	5.6	4 months	2	good
year	2.10	5 weeks	2	fair
months	3.1	9 months	2	good
weeks	4.10	1 month	3	nil
5 months	2.1	6 months	2	nil
months			1	nil
o record	4.2	no record	several	nil
veral days	4.10	several days	2	nil

Fair, if part-time. E.g. Nursery Nurses doing other duties.
No provision at all.

Doll-play projective test

(cont. from p. 111)
Only the first one is marked in categories, as an example of the method used.

1. Children from hospitals with no play provision. B.

David, aged five years, the second of two children, was born with talipes, which was operated on when he was two years old. He contracted polio one day after his discharge from hospital and was in an isolation hospital for six weeks. His mother died of cancer while he was again in hospital at the age of two years, eleven months. His grandmother now looks after the family, aided by a very devoted young father. Two months previous to testing he had had an operation on his right foot. He wore double callipers and used a walking stick but was very independent and determined. He was of average intelligence, a real 'rumbustious' boy in spite of his disability. He had to be carried upstairs but insisted on walking down, a considerable physical effort for him. There was no play provision in either of the hospitals in which he was a patient.

EXTRACTS

Session 1

    Walked nurse round the ward pushing trolley. Walked nurse away./   Th.

D. 'This is a new one coming in with Mummy and Daddy'. Girl 2 with mother and father. Puts Girl 2 to bed./   Th.

D. Examined mother. 'This ain't a real scarf. Look Dad has fair hair./ My Dad works knocking buildings   E. down. When I get big I'm going to help him. I'm going to drive a crane'./   T.

    Walked father and mother to bedside of Boy 1.

D. 'They're visiting'.

Gave them a chair./ Put fruit from trolley on locker.   Th.
Nurse pushed trolley and knocked over the doctor.

D. 'She doesn't look where she's going./ I've got a toy-   Th.
shop and Karen's (sister) got a hospital. I like it. The
nurse winds up and moves and makes a noise./   T.
Mummy and Daddy are going now. They're waiting for the bus'. Made bus noises./   Th.

D. 'The boy is getting up, he's going to the toilet. He's
creeping'.
Made Boy 1 climb on trolley, then stand at back of
wall. Put him back in cot.

D. 'He wants Mummy and Daddy. Here they come./   Th.
Look they've put a little boy in a big bed'. (Baby 1
in cot.) Turned cot up on end and tipped baby out.

D. 'Look he's chucked his cot up sideways, he's got out
of it, he don't like it. This little baby is coming
home. It can't stand up./ My aunt got a little baby'.   I.Th.
Picked up locker.   T.

D. 'I know what these are for—toothpaste and tooth
brushes and toys. Why ain't the little boy got one?
I'll give him this one (taken from Girl 2), because
she's going home./ There she goes up in the air—   O.
she ain't got to go back no more./ This is a new one   I.Th.
coming——.

Session 4

Examined chairs and trolley. Took nurse to trolley. Put
father on chair—took him off and bent him backwards.

D. 'Look how fat he is. Ole fatty! Two fatties (Doing likewise to doctor). They're flying'.
Bent mother and put her on one chair and Boy 2 on
other chair.

D. 'They're going to bed now. Where's the other baby?'
(using a tiny voice).

Doll-play projective test

Put Girl 1 in Cot 3, then asked for other bed. Put Boy 1 in Bed 4. Put father on chair by Boy 2.

D. 'He's out of bed, he's going somewhere (Boy 2). They're only toys ain't they?'

Took walls away and put on floor.

D. 'I'm taking these away so a bit of light can come'.

Took Boy 2 to cot, then to centre of ward.

D. 'His girl friend has to come—here she is'—they kiss (making appropriate noises).

D. 'He's going to jump out (doctor) round the room, he ain't getting back'.

Put mother in chair by Girl 2.

'Nurse says, "I'm running away over the other side".'

Nurse attacked sister, making rude noises.

D. 'Sister's going back to her office' (taking sister to far side of room).

Made sister dance on big table at far side of room. Took her all round room. (*N.B.*—David has double calipers and all this roaming around the room was a considerable effort for him.) Back to model.

D. 'This is the ward being made. I got to make them properly. Put the beds and chairs here. They all being muddled up. Is that how he was sitting? (Putting father on chair by cot side.) The cot's got to be done, (pulling cot side out). Where's the mother? She's going now, she's putting her baby back. Say mother, mummy, mummy! (Babyish calling.) Got to have a top on her, (laying cot side over top of cot). She's still going in her cot. She drop's the baby. Oh, my head! The baby's running away from hospital'. (Crawling away on floor with baby.)

T. 'What will nurse do?'

D. 'Come and find her'.

Sister looked in cot.

D. 'Oh, where's the other one gone? Oh, I find you. I warned you. You're coming back with me (carrying baby under sister's arm). You get back in your bed', (fiercely).
Sister fell on top of Boy 2.

D. 'She's trying to get up but she can't. She's still trying to get up. She (Girl 1) runs away like a snail. She's going to fly and she'll fall and blow up. (Throwing Girl 1 around the room.) I'm getting back in my cot (putting Girl 1 in cot). Shut that side'.——

David was a very energetic, forthright little boy and his play was deliberate and lively. He was very willing to go with the tester at the first session. Having identified the ward and the dolls he lost no time in beginning to play. In his play there were several references to going home and not coming back any more, to running away and to visiting. These, together with play concerning babies in cots, were generally followed by some kind of tangential behaviour, such as exploration, organization, or definite withdrawal. There was one rather bizarre piece of behaviour occurring in the last two sessions; the father, and on one occasion the doctor, was bent backwards, jeered at and called 'ole fatty' and made to fly through the air. After due reflection this was categorized as individualized thematic rather than tangential play as the tester had the impression that this theme was bound up with David's physical disability, his desire to be free of his callipers and as strong as his much admired dad. In the third session David was rather listless but his fourth was remarkable for his great expenditure of sheer physical energy; he was literally throwing himself around the room. He appeared to be in high good humour at the end of this session. David's test shows a high percentage of individualized thematic play.

Joseph, aged four years, six months, a West Indian, the youngest of five children, contracted polio at the age of eight months, when he was in hospital for sixteen months, during which time his mother visited frequently, except for a period of one month, when she disappeared and could not be found. Joseph was readmitted to hospital at the age of two years, one month for a further six months. Both the isolation hospital to which he was initially admitted and the children's hospital to which he was transferred had no play provision.

Joseph was assessed as having average intelligence. His teacher said that he was a quiet lovable little boy with a very difficult aggressive family.

He wore double callipers and walked with great difficulty. He had to be carried up the stairs.

Joseph was a very quiet, apparently timid little boy, who only spoke in a whisper throughout the tests. His teacher had told him that he must talk to the tester and he made a great effort to do so in his first sessions but as time went on he became more and more absorbed in his play and spoke less. Many of his remarks were completely inaudible.

EXTRACTS
Session 1

Examined Girl 2.

J. 'You're going home. Don't be a naughty girl. You're going in bed. She's fall off. (Callously.) What you doing there?' Tipped up all beds. Piled all children on floor. Sister kicked children.

J. 'She's pushing them down'.
Made doctor and sister dance. Pushed them down on heap of children.

J. 'Can kick—been a naughty girl. Push them down. Where's nurse?'

Examined nurse, tried to pull off cap with side glance at

tester. Stood up doctor. Examined sister's cap. Stood
sister and doctor together by trolley.

J. 'Doctor shoots sister. She's dead. I hate you nurse.'
Brought father to sister. Doctor walked father off.

J. 'Don't kick.'
Doctor walked on father. Tipped up all beds. (All this
done quite amiably.)

J. 'You're going home in bed.'
End of session.

Session 3

Boy 1 knocked down all standing figures.

Boy 1 lifted up doctor.

Put all figures lying in a row, heads and feet alternate.
Wheeled trolley, pushing Boy 1 with it. Wheeled trolley
round and round line of figures lying on the floor,
eventually pushing babies and mother with it. Wheeled
and knocked over trolley. Put Baby 1 on trolley and tried
to put Baby 2 on lower shelf—failed—put both on top
and made them fall off.

Pushed chair around group of figures on floor. Put Baby 1
under the chair and pushed him around.

Arranged figures in line on floor. Walked Girl 2 round.
Tipped up all the beds and cots in turn.

Boy 1 walked slowly to figures on floor and touched
heads of each in turn, then kicked and stamped on them.
Put sister and doctor in beds. Tried to put father in cot and
took him out. Tried to force nurse into cot. Put father
standing in cot with nurse—father kicking nurse.

Lined up figures in groups of three on the floor.

Took doctor to Boy 1 knocking him over. Doctor kicked
nurse over, kicked baby. Arranged figures top to toe again.
Put chair on top of sister and pushed around making a

chug! chug! sound.
Picked up Girl 2 and dropped her from a height, then
picked her up and stood her on a chair, whispering.
Grouped cots and stood them on end, and put babies in
them in this position.
Put Boy 1 and Girl 1 together in a cot.
Piled up lockers.
End of session.

Joseph came very willingly to the first session and once the
dolls were identified he started to play without any further
encouragement. At first his play was largely exploratory and
organizational and the children were put to bed, but as time
went on, the adults were put to bed. Towards the end of the
session there was a good deal of aggressive play, as the extract
shows. The appearance of the ward was decidedly chaotic at
the end. He was very anxious lest he should miss his turn for
the second session and began to play immediately, again making the dolls show a great deal of aggression to each other. All
these aggressive acts were carried out quietly and deliberately
but with no visible signs of anger. At the beginning of his
third session Joseph spent some time standing the dolls in a
line and interchanging them. This was followed by a series of
aggressive acts, each of which was followed up by some form
of lining up and ritual pattern-making with the toys. Joseph's
play was much quieter this time, he did not speak at all. He
was quite naughty on his return to the classroom and burst
out crying when he was rebuked by his teacher. At the beginning of the fourth session he handled the toys very gently, but
as time went on he repeated the pattern of aggressive acts
followed by some form of ritual arrangement of the toys.
Again all the aggressive acts were carried out quietly, with an
intent but smiling face, accompanied by inaudible whispering.

The main characteristic of Joseph's play was the amount of

aggression, 22·8 per cent, all carried out with an air of quiet deliberation and with no change of facial expression or feeling of viciousness about it. One almost felt that in Joseph's world people did indeed kick and stamp on each other. His 'ward' was always in a state of complete chaos at the end of each session. He showed a high percentage, 34·9 per cent, of individualized thematic play. This, and the aggression, was generally followed by some form of organizational behaviour, usually consisting of arranging the figures head to toe in a row or a circle, or sometimes in pairs with the head of one wedged between the legs of another. This was categorized as random manipulation or withdrawal.

John, aged four years, suffering from hydrocephalus following meningitis, was an only child from a good home. He was in hospital, where no special play facilities were provided, for several months during his second year. The educational psychologist who tested him on his admission to the school has queried his educability, but he had a good vocabulary, clear speech and on the whole appeared to play aptly and purposefully. He did occasionally give the impression of being slightly deaf, but his teacher said that this had never been suggested. She described him as a lovable engaging little rascal who had a rather disruptive influence on his nursery group and was very destructive.

John was an eager, excitable little boy, always anxious to come for his turn and his sessions were notable for the feverish activity of his play and the amount of verbalization.

EXTRACTS
Session 1
J. 'Look at man (father) he fell out of bed—he's dead now. She gone in cot (Girl 1). Oh, she's fell out of cot. All

childrens go to bed now (putting children in bed). Where's mummy gone? There she is (picking her up). All childrens to bed'.
Moved lockers. Tipped Girl 2 out of bed.

J. 'She's fell out of bed. She not going to bed now'.
Stacked beds one on another.

J. 'Not childrens going to bed now. He going to have a ride (putting Boy 1 on trolley). Nurse come and push (picks up Girl 1). She going to have needle. She going to bed right now (puts in bed). Where's mummy?. Where's the chair? (Picks up babies.) They're going to bed now. (Picks up mother.) Oh, the chair fall down. She (mummy) going home (fiercely to babies). Your mummy going home'.
Put mother in cot and showed great glee when she fell out.

J. 'They're not going to bed are they?' (Babies.).
End of session.

Session 3

J. 'She not well (Sister). She crying—she feel poorly. She feel poorly (nurse). Sh! You'll wake all the childrens up. (Puts children to bed.) All the childrens going to bed now—they're going to have their breakfast. You push the breakfast (nurse pushing trolley). Here comes breakfast. Do you want some breakfast (to sister in bed). There you are, sit up! She don't want it now—empty it all away. Got two chairs. Where's the other chairs gone? Oh, they fall on the mother in the bed. Oh, the boy . . .' banging Boy 2's feet.
Nurse and Boy 2 jumped up and down together, jumped

J. on bed, fall off. Nurse stood up and knocked down. 'Oh, quick, hold her, she going to fall, she bump her head. There goes the bed (throwing the bed down). They're not going to bed now 'cos we're going to take them away now'. (Piling beds.)

Wanted to go and went to door and opened it. Tester encouraged him to return. He went out of the door, closed it, then after a minute, opened it and came back again.

J. 'Put the three beds there. Three cots there. All the babies going to sleep. They're crying. (Picked up Baby 1 and cradled it in his arms.) Sh! Sh! This baby's crying. Sh! They're going to sleep—they're going to sleep. Sh!' Sings 'Baa, baa black sheep' all through.

J. 'They're not going to bed. They're going to stay there. (Children on the floor.) They all fall down (piling lockers).' Found that cot sides came out and spent the rest of the time taking them out and putting them back.

End of session.

Session 4

J. 'They're not going to bed, they're not going to bed now. (Piling the cots one on another.) Put the cots away, eh? They fall'. (Cots crash down to his great excitement.) Gathers all the dolls into his arms.

J. 'They're all my children. You don't touch my childrens. You won't touch my childrens will you? (vehemently). Take the beds away—take all the beds away. (Piling beds and cots.) They fall again (shouting)'. Gathered all the furniture and dolls into his arms, saying defiantly:

J. 'They're all mine, you're not going to touch them. I make a piano eh? (puts three lockers together). I sing Baa, baa, black sheep now. (This he did, pretending to play the piano and swaying in his chair.) I knock them down (throwing lockers). All the childrens are crying, look. Make it all better eh. (Loves them better.) (Picks up father.) He fall out the bed, he dead'.

123

Doll-play projective test

Doctor and father fight.

J. 'They fight—they fall down. You shoot him—bang! bang! they fall dead. They not crying look, they going to fight now. (Jumping and banging the doctor and father together.) He hurt his legs—look. Make it better. Two legs are better——'

John came very eagerly to his first session, chattering all the time. He could hardly wait to have the dolls identified and began to play precipitately, maintaining a feverish activity throughout. There were eight references to children or adults falling out of bed and two to the nurse having a needle. The second session was also very active though there was an interval of aimless play with the cot side. Again there were six references to children falling out of bed. Twice the children were said to be crying but the question 'Why are they crying?' was ignored. In the third session he withdrew from the material altogether, but returned, as the extract shows. For the fourth session John came eagerly as usual and began to play immediately. He was very noisy and excited throughout the session, at one point gathering all the toys into his arms, saying defiantly 'They're all mine, you're not going to touch them!'. There was a good deal of aggressive play both with dolls and furniture. This fourth session brought a feeling of mounting aggression and excitement.

The recurring theme of falling out of bed and bumping heads seemed to express some underlying anxiety, but this may well be linked up with his hydrocephalus and his slightly enlarged head, perhaps allied with some residual feeling of insecurity connected with hospitalization. A more overtly expressed anxiety was that of the needle. There were several references to babies crying but any question on the subject was ignored. There was a tendency to put the adults to bed instead of the children. John shows a high percentage, 47 per cent, of individualized thematic play. He also shows a comparatively high percentage, 13·2 per cent, of aggression.

Mary, aged five years, suffered from chronic osteomyelitis, and had a history of frequent hospitalization. She came from a fairly good home and was of average intelligence, but both mother and teacher found her a very difficult child. She was said to be lovable but demanding and her teacher reported that she had a disruptive influence on the class. She was very active and had severe temper tantrums when crossed. She could be extremely defiant in these moods, using a good deal of bad language.

Mary was usually eager to come for her sessions but did very little with the material. The little play that she did carry out was remarkable for its feverish intensity.

EXTRACTS

Session 2

Was not very anxious to come, but agreed after some hesitation. Began to play at once.

M. 'Who's this—the nurse? We got another one (Sister). Will she sit on the chair? She have to have the baby' (sitting baby on sister's knee).

Put baby in mother's arms. Stood up the other adults, put Boy 2 on trolley, likewise Girl 2. Put both babies in one cot. Mother carried Girl 2 to bed, then carried first the father and then the doctor pick-a-back fashion to bed— lay them across beds.

M. 'Where's the mummy gone? She's going to carry this one —no, the nurse is. There you are. Now she's carrying the mummy. (Nurse forcing the mother into bed.) The babies are going to go with their mummy'.

After this Mary roamed round the room examining tester's

handbag and picking up various articles. She asked to be allowed to use some coloured chalks from a shelf and when refused wanted to return to her classroom. She could not be persuaded to play with the dolls, so she was allowed to go, suggesting that she come another time, to which she agreed. End of session.

Session 3

Asked to come before it was her turn. Began to play without encouragement.

Arranged furniture. Put babies in cot.

M. 'The baby's crying'.

T. 'Who will comfort her?'

M. 'The daddy'.

Turned away from the dolls and asked to be allowed to draw. Could not be persuaded to play and so 'drew' for the rest of the session. This consisted of filling up pages with squiggles. Insisted on having name put on each page.

Session 4

Ran to tester and asked to come. Began feverishly to play. Put all the children in bed. Moved lockers.

M. 'I put them like this sometimes. Can I put them like this sometimes (fitting lockers together). I can make beds of these. Can you keep them up please (pile of lockers).'

Lockers fell—abandoned. Arranged beds.

M. 'Here's the table what they go out with. I'm putting the babies under there (lockers). Can I draw now?'.

Here tester suggested that Mary played a little longer before drawing.

Pulled cots forward and put babies in.

M. 'One goes there. One lay down. Look at them, they laying down. Mummy's coming in a minute. I want to go back to my classroom now'.

Tester again persuaded her to play.

M. 'Look, here they all are sitting in one cot. Please may I draw now?'.

Spent the rest of the session 'drawing' the same squiggles. Tidied the ward before she left but insisted on leaving the babies in their cots.

Mary showed an extremely high percentage, 68·1 per cent, of tangential behaviour, and it was difficult to decide whether this was part of her normal pattern of restless behaviour or a reaction to the material, indicating a deep-seated disturbance related to the hospital situation. There seemed to be no definite pattern to her play although the withdrawal often followed some reference to the baby, in the cot, being with her mummy, or crying. She played to the end of the first session but withdrew after ten minutes in the second. She asked to come first for the third session but turned away from the material after five minutes and spent the rest of the time 'drawing'. She played feverishly for five minutes in the fourth session, withdrew, played for a few more minutes when encouraged by tester, but then returned to her 'drawing' again. This drawing consisted of pages of circular squiggles.

James, aged five years, nine months, suffered from haemophilia from which his only brother died. He was in hospital at four years, nine months, and again at four years, ten months, for eighteen days. This hospital makes no play provision. He was of Indian extraction from a fairly good home, but very much over-protected because of the nature of his disease and the death of his brother. Mother told of temper tantrums at home but his teacher said that there was no sign of these at school where he was very quiet and obedient. He did some very good imaginative painting.

Doll-play projective test

He appeared to be a very quiet, reserved little boy and the tester was not able to make much contact with him.

EXTRACTS
Session 1

Came willingly, but a little solemnly. Began to play immediately, in a rather desultory manner.

Put Boy 1 in bed, Boy 2 in cot, tried Girl 1 first in cot and then in bed, Girl 2 in bed and then in cot.

Put babies in cots. Touched the trolley and chairs in turn. Took father to chair and then to locker. Fingered mother hesitantly. Took father to mother and made him touch her foot gently. Moved mother and father to trolley. Took sister and nurse to trolley and made them push it.

T. 'What's on the trolley?' Shook head.

Took doctor to Boy 1 in bed and made him lean over, then to Girl 2 and lean over, to cots and lean over each in turn (very absorbed play now).

T. 'What is he doing?'

J. 'Examining their chests'.

Doctor leaned over trolley.

T. 'What is he doing?'.

J. 'The boy's going to have an operation'.

T. 'Does he mind?'.

J. 'Yes' (tiny almost inaudible voice).

Doctor plied between bed and trolley in realistic imitation of operation. Bed put back against wall, trolley back to centre of ward, doctor to stand against wall. Mother and father brought to Boy 1 in bed, then father taken to doctor.

J. 'He says he'll be better in a week's time'.

Piled lockers on chair, made sister climb to top and down and then doctor to top and stand.

J. 'He's getting some medicine'.

Brought doctor down, to trolley, back to stand on lockers, made him fall down and laughed, climb back again, and fall again. Put lockers back in place. Put mother and father behind screen. Took mother to nurse, they appear to quarrel, took mother back behind screen. Piled lockers up again and chair on top. Made doctor climb up and stand on top. Mother brought in and made to feign kick at lockers (with sideways glance at tester who smiled encouragingly). Made mother kick lockers over and doctor fell down. Father came to help push him over.

J. 'He has to have an operation now (gleefully).' Put doctor in bed and sister and nurse by him. Put father and mother on top of doctor in bed. Laid sister on one locker and nurse on other. Lined up cots end to end. Put Girl 2 on trolley.

End of session.

Session 3

Did not seem very eager to come and spent some time looking around him before beginning to play, slowly and reluctantly.

Put children to bed with right hand while holding doctor in left. Put nurse to bed.

Hesitated over beds, then turned nurse out and put boy in. Put father and nurse face to face (conversation?).

Examined sister. Put sister and mother face to face, then sister and doctor. Examined doctor. Stood sister on chair. Took doctor to trolley. Put doctor and sister together on chair, blew sister off chair. Put sister and nurse together, then doctor and nurse together, then father and doctor together. Straightened father. Stacked lockers—hesitated —put doctor on top of lockers. Took him off to trolley.

I

Put father on chair. Bent doctor and tried to sit him on chair. Tidied lockers away. Asked to return to classroom. End of session.

James's records show a reversal of the usual building up towards a freer display of aggression at the end of the fourth session. He began to show a good deal of inhibition during the third session, withdrawing completely after ten minutes, and in the fourth produced entirely organizational or tangential behaviour and again withdrew completely after ten minutes.

In the earlier sessions he had a recurring theme of piling up the lockers, standing the doctor on top and either pushing him off deliberately or arranging for him to fall and then putting him to bed. This was usually followed by some organizational play. In the third session he made a tentative move to repeat this pattern but withdrew from it and did not make it in.

This may have been because the material failed to hold his interest or it could be that he had already worked through his problems in the earlier sessions.

Children from hospitals with some play provision. (A)
Edward, aged seven years, had had frequent periods of three to four weeks duration in hospital owing to rectal agenesis, and several operations, the earliest being at four years old. He had just returned to school after a four-week stay in hospital, when he had a colostomy. His teacher said that he was so disturbed at this readmission to hospital that he had to have psychotherapy before he could be treated medically. He was an only child from a good home, and of normal intelligence. He was small for his age.

The hospital in which he was treated employs nursery nurses, but these do not always carry out 'play therapy'.

Edward was a very quiet reserved little boy, at first quite unsmiling and apparently unresponsive although he came to play willingly.

EXTRACTS

Session 1

   Took doctor to Boy 2 in bed.

T. 'What is he doing?'

E. 'He's listening to his chest.'
   Brought mother and father into ward. Moved nurse to bed—Girl 1.

T. 'What is she doing?'

E. 'Seeing if the poor little girl is all right. That's sister—she's putting dinner round. There's all babies (pointing to cots).'

T. 'What are they doing?'

E. 'One little girl is resting, one baby is asleep and one is awake.'
   Took doctor to cot.
   'He just fits over that. I wish we had an operation trolley.'
   (Tester suggested pretending ward trolley was operation trolley, Edward shook his head. Tester then suggested pushing bed as trolley—also rejected.)

E. 'I know, pretend this little girl got up in dressing-gown (picking up Girl 1). Nurse is making her bed.'

T. 'Is she glad to be up?'

E. 'Not yet—she's got to have an operation.'——

E. ——'Did you make them? Make another little boy and then his mummy and daddy could bring him in.'
   Took nurse to talk to mother and father.

E. 'Does she want anything to eat? Daddy has to leave now. Oh, no, he don't 'cos he's talking to the doctor. When is my little girl coming home? I don't know. He's calling Sister (moving doctor to sister and murmuring). O.K.

131

Sister says she can go home. This one can't go home yet,
(Girl 2). She's only just come in.'
Examined label on Girl 2 and wanted to know what it said.

T. 'Made in England.'

E. 'Yes, some toys do come from England and some come
from Harringay. I live in Harringay.'
Took Boy 1 to trolley.

E. 'I want that one nurse. Nurse, says no, lay down or I shall
hit you.'
Examined cot.

E. 'Nurse is taking baby for a bath.'
End of session.

Session 4

E. 'That's funny look.' (Indicating space between beds.)
'You could make Sister's desk with a locker.'
Put sister by locker. Took Girl 2 to sister at desk, making
her speak in a baby voice (unintelligible). Made a tele-
phone ringing noise—Sister answered.

E. 'Yes, who is it? What did you say? (crossly).'
Nurse stood on desk—Sister pulled her off. Pushed Girl 1
on to locker (desk) shelf.

E. 'You naughty girl! (pushing girl in locker round ward).
She pushed the bed down. Let's get the baby out. Mamma!
Where's that? (Discovering that cot side is movable.)
Naughty little girl—squash her under the side. Why did
you have to fall out of bed?'
Took doctor to baby in cot—put the side up. Took a chair
to the doctor.

E. 'Sister's taking the baby's stitches out.'
Put cot back in place, singing. Put baby in Bed 1 and Boy
1 in cot. Father kicked Girl 2 and Boy 2 over and walked
on them. Examined cot again. Sister took Girl 1 to cot.

E. 'This is how you have them down sometimes (indicating cot side). What's the matter?' (Sister to baby in cot).

Put baby in cot on bed, another bed on top and another cot on top of that, saying 'Look!' with a pleased smile. Put Boy 2 in top bed and all fell over. Made Boy 2 and father fight. Piled beds up again, laughing. Nurse took the babies out of the cots.

E. 'They're going to watch. He sits there' (putting babies on chairs).

Piled beds and other children up and took them down several times.

End of session.

Edward needed a good deal of encouragement at the beginning of the first session and spent his time in examination and organization, quite concerned about the realism of the material. Only towards the end did he appear to be expressing his feelings. He came smilingly to the second session. Again he was rather concerned with realism and again any expression of feelings came towards the end. This latter was mainly aggression, followed by lining the dolls up on the floor and counting them. He was still rather tense. At the third session he came running eagerly when he saw the tester and began to play immediately, needing no encouragement throughout the session. His play was much more lively and a good deal of aggression was shown, followed by lining up the dolls. He was also eager to come for his fourth session and handled the toys in an easy and casual way, in contrast to the careful, timid approach of the first session. Again there was a good deal of aggression.

Edward played quietly and deliberately throughout, showing a fair percentage of thematic play (24 per cent). His approach became increasingly bolder and his play became increasingly aggressive as the sessions progressed. He was also much more friendly and relaxed with the tester and

133

one felt that he had in some way been released by the test.

Anne, aged four years, eleven months, the fourth of five children from an overcrowded, discordant home, had been admitted to hospital on six different occasions for periods of several weeks, owing to fragile bones. The first hospitalization was at two years, six months, to a hospital which employs nursery nurses and the subsequent admissions to a hospital where no special provision is made, but where there is a pleasant, permissive atmosphere. She had had seven fractures in two years, her last hospitalization being at the age of three years, ten months.

Anne was superficially very friendly and a talkative little girl, a typical much hospitalized child.

EXTRACTS
Session 1
   Wheeled trolley round ward.
A. 'There's dinner for you. There's dinner for you—(repeated all round ward). They're skinny cots in our hospital.' (Picking cot up.) Nurse taken round ward.
A. 'Did you have any dinner? Yes. (Repeated all round.) There's a mummy and there's a nurse. Did you have any dinner? (Repeated.) No! What did you say?' (Sharply.) Wheeled trolley again to beds in turn.
A. 'There's the nurse. There's mummy. Did you have any dinner (angrily). No! (rudely). She mustn't do this.' Sister jumped on nurse's head. Sister examined.
A. 'This isn't real hair.'
   Examined mother.
A. 'Will the bag come off? They'll sit down all right won't they? They ain't got all chairs have they? She won't sit down all right,' trying to make mother sit on chair.
A. 'Have you been a good girl. Have you been a good boy?'
134

Session 2

Sat Girl 2 up in bed 3. boy 2 in bed 2. Boy 1 in bed 4.

A. 'Put you over there. Come on baby we'll sit you up. She likes sitting up. Sometimes I say Oh! blimey when they fall down (watching for reaction from tester). You sit up (Girl 1). You're going to have a wonderful meal. You're going in a big bed. Make the little baby sit.' (Boy 1 in Cot 2.) Tried to put doctor and then nurse in cot. Nurse pushed cot.

A. 'Put that up' (sitting Boy 2 up in cot). 'If mummy buys some of these toys dad will go mad. He don't like toys. Mum does.'

Picked up Baby 2 and examined.

A. 'Her foots bited—this is strong plastic, it won't bend. Only the babies won't bend. Lucy is going to sit up now——'

A. 'I got a big doll at home and it's got a cot——'

T. (Drawing attention back to test.) 'What happens next?'

Mother sat on chair nursing Baby 1.

A. 'Bet the doctor's after her to get her leg done. She'll have to get the leg done else she'll have to go in an ambulance. Our baby is called Lucy Theresa (a good deal of talk about her own family followed).'

T. 'What is the baby doing?'

A. 'She's sitting on her mum's lap.'

Put baby back in cot. Picked up Baby 2.

Session 3

A. 'There's the two babies. I don't think these can sit up. She sits all right (Girl 1). This can sit up (Baby 1). Our Lucy has diemonia (*sic*!). (More chat about her own family followed.) Here's father—he goes walking—his head's broken—it could be your baby broken. The nurse is

135

standing up. The mother's standing up. Hey! put your legs straight!'

Much energetic twisting of mother's legs.

A. 'Daddy brings toys and then throws them out. Mummy says I want new clothes but Daddy don't care about them. All he cares about is mending, mending, mending.'

Encouraged by Observer to turn attention to test again.

A. 'Nurse is going to push the trolley. Lucy has got special food and she's in a special room.' (More chat about family.) Turned her attention back to nurse, straightened her legs.

A. 'Put your legs straight. She's the smallest nurse I ever saw before. This boy's pyjamas are the same as her dress. I saw a boy like that in my hospital. She won't stand straight for me. (Sister.) I wouldn't dare break her now.' Strayed off into chat about her special friend——.

A. 'He's in his clothes (Boy 2) and he's in his clothes (Boy 1). This is Lucy Theresa (baby). This is made of strong plastic. Is that your book? (Observer's notebook.) We had a book like that in hospital and we could write in it. I was going to write about Lucy. He's a big boy ain't he? These are her two babies (mother). This little girl can walk can't she? (Girl 1.) Do you know when my Ian (brother) went to see me in hospital do you know what he done—he broke the window thing and Sister been after him—that's what she should do shouldn't she? When I first started to come out of this bed I had to kick—they wanted me to learn girl's football. And you will go home too (Girl 2). You'll be able to stand won't you? Let's see if you will stand.'

End of session.

Session 4

Picked up nurse.

A. 'I'm going to learn myself to be a school nurse, you have to pour out milk and you have straws.'
Again went on to talk about what they had at home.
Once more encouraged to return to model.

A. 'Put all the children in bed. You in there (Boy 1). You're a bit too little for that bed. You'll go in there—that'll fit you won't it? The baby go in there. Hey, don't you fall! We'll put you on top there (put cot side on top and baby on this). She should be a bit bigger though. She's afraid she's going to fall out. Put you here in this cot—this is a safety cot (putting side of cot up and down). Here, say this was Lucy. This is a funny way I dreamed last night (cots piled one on another) and they all falled down. There's not another safety one is there? We're going to put all the beds in a row, small cots too—they're going to have a picture taken. When I was little I crawled out of bed because I had a bad toe and Daddy wouldn't believe it. All the children are sitting up in bed. Let's put the trolley here. Now where shall we put you (Girl 2)? All you facing that way please.'

Anne's sessions were both difficult to record and to categorize. Her play was very spasmodic and disjointed, with very many digressions and much verbalization, so much so that it was impossible to record it all. Everything was carried out at speed. References to her home and family were frequent and one felt that the home situation was so disturbing that it overlaid all her play. Her frequent allusions to Lucy, her baby sister, gave one the impression that Anne was identifying with her, consequently these references have been counted as identification. Apart from relating everything to her home background, there was no very clear pattern of play. Such hospital themes as she did play out were almost entirely thematic. Her fourth session was particularly full of digressions and Anne needed much encouragement to keep her mind on the material.

Anne showed a high percentage of exploratory and organizational play, 17·3 per cent and 27·2 per cent; a fair percentage of thematic, 14·8 per cent; and very little individualized thematic, only 4·9 per cent; while she also shows the highest percentage, 13·6 per cent, of identification.

Sarah, aged six years, five months, came from a large happy family whose mother was Indian. She had polio at three years and was in hospital for several months. She was readmitted at five years, six months for four months. The hospital was one where nursery play is provided.

She was a happy alert little girl, very heavily handicapped, wearing double callipers and using elbow crutches. She was of average intelligence. Her teacher said that she was co-operative and lively.

Sarah, a very friendly and talkative six-year-old, played with purpose and concentration. The material made an immediate impact on her and she needed no introduction to it. She kept up a running commentary all the time. She was always very eager to come for her turn, and indeed at the third session she was so eager that she omitted to go to the lavatory, with a resulting accident which she ignored until the play session was ended.

EXTRACTS
Session 1
S. 'She's going to take this' (nurse, taking trolley).
T. 'What is on the trolley?'
S. 'Operation things. The father is going to have an operation. She's seeing to the baby (Sister to Boy 1) he's got poorly legs. She's going to make them better. Now she's

138

going to the babies. She's going to pick them up now.
Now she's going to lay her down. Father's had his operation, the girl (Girl 1) is bringing fruit and flowers. She's
got to take her little sister. I used to be in hospital a long
time ago. *They're* not well now. (Nurse and Sister.) He's
better (father). His little girl is going to him and the big
sister. She's not well now (putting nurse to bed with mischievous smile). He's going home now (father) take his
little girls—Oh dear she falls, now she not well, they have
to go to bed.' (Girls.)

T. 'Who will look after them?'
S. 'Their father.'
Examined trolley.
S. 'Now the doctor's going to the girl—she's going to have
an operation. She doesn't mind. Now which bed are we
going to empty?'
Stood mother in cot with baby.
S. 'Now she's happy. When I was in a cot some of the
childrens used to come like this in my cot. The boy (Boy
1) is jumping on the chair. Which was my bed. He needs a
bed. This was my locker. He comes to the locker and
takes his clothes out and changes to go home. They all
better now. (Standing all the dolls up.) They all happy
now because they better and the doctor's better. Oh he's
fallen down! She was still lying down (finding Girl 2 in
cot). All the beds are empty now aren't they? The hospital's all empty now—the nurse has to stay. These four
childrens has to stay.' (Babies and girls.) Put babies in cots
—stood cots up on end.
S. 'Look, two of them are standing up—the baby and her
sister. Now the visitors are coming. The childrens got to
go to bed. The mummy and daddy's got to come. His
mother's not coming (Boy 1) he's got to have an opera-

139

tion. They've got to move the beds and cots, the children mustn't see. They can see, can't they? The children stand up on the beds to see. They all can see. Oh no, what about these children (in the cots) that's not fair.'

Session 2

Sat father and mother on chairs.

S. 'They're going to change chairs. These are two sisters (babies). They're better now. These babies are hers (mother's). They're all better now. They're all out now. Now how could they all go. They each go to one. He takes the boy first (father) and the mother takes her—now she's going to pick her up (mother carried Girl 2). Now they're going out. Now she have to get picked up (Girl 1). The mother and father carry her. They're not in hospital now, they're home.'

Session 3

Came in from treatment to find me waiting for her—very anxious lest she miss her turn. Sat down and started to play at once.

Picked up Mother and Father.

S. 'They're coming—these are the visitors. They're all getting ready. Only the babies could go in there (the cots) and she's not a baby is she? (Mother.) Nurse goes on the chair. The doctor won't stand up will he? He's going to sit on a chair. (Here Sarah had an 'accident' but ignored it and went on playing with complete absorption.) He needs a chair to sit down and do operations. (Putting chair by trolley.) She's (Girl 2) going to put clothes on and run to her Mummy. Look, she's pickened her up—she takes her. She have to hold her haven't she?——'

S. 'Now what shall I do? Put this nurse sitting on the chair or Sister because she's going to help the doctor. Now she's helping the doctor and Staff's going to bring the operation things (nurse with trolley). She comes out and she's going to stay standing there and now what of the mother and father. They open this door. His Mummy's come. (Boy 10 Oh, the boy's fallen down—he have to sit on this side because he's had an operation. We must have some screens to put round so they can't see (moved walls to make screen round Girl 2 in bed). The visitors is comed now and what can be the baby's Mummy? She can hold on the boy can't she? (Putting mother on Boy 1's bed.) My Mummy used to bring flowers for me in hospital and I had two operations. Now she could sit down can't she? (mother) and father can sit down (putting both on chairs). Oh, the boy was getting off. He can sit next to the boy can't he? (Father.) Now they've finished the operation (moving screens away).——'

Sarah showed the highest percentage of thematic play, 46·2 per cent. Her hospital themes were mostly apt, apart from the adults occasionally being put to bed and given operations. The idea of going to hospital to be made well, and of being taken home by parents when better, was firmly expressed. Mother and father played a large part, and there were references to visiting and looking after the children. She had 7·7 per cent of identification, all references to her own hospitalization being made very happily and with no suggestion of anxiety. There were many references to operations and the children were said not to mind having them. There was, however, one recurring theme where a child had an operation behind a screen and Sarah showed some concern as to whether the children could see. Although because of the continuity and aptness of the theme, this was labelled thematic play, it could well have had an element of underlying anxiety. She showed no aggression at all.

Doll-play projective test

Ronnie, aged five years, had polio at one year and was in hospital for one year. He was again hospitalized at two years, ten months for five weeks with tonsillitis and meningeal symptoms. He was left with no physical disability but was recommended for a school for the physically handicapped because he was excessively timid. He was the second of two children from a good home, of average intelligence and had now become, according to his teacher, noisy and aggressive, though he was very shy and quiet with the tester.

He was at a hospital which employs nursery nurses for general duties.

EXTRACTS

Session 1

Jumped up eagerly to come, but did not talk on the way. Ran to table and sat down. Tester identified dolls. No comment. Looked rather unhappy.

Examined Girl 1 and stood up.

Examined Girl 2 and stood up.

Examined Boy 1 and stood up.

Examined Boy 2 and stood up.

Stood babies up. Looked around. Put Girl 1 in bed, Boy 1 in cot, Boy 2 in cot, Girl 2 in cot. Picked up Boy 1—hesitated and put in bed. Put Boy 2 in bed. After encouragement took mother and father to Boy 1 in cot. More encouragement. Took sister to trolley—wheeled trolley tentatively. Put sister back with nurse and doctor in row in middle of ward. Silence and hesitation—appeared very inhibited and not very happy. After encouragement picked up sister, took her to trolley and wheeled trolley. Put sister back in row in middle of ward. Examined trolley—wheeled round to end of cot along ends of beds and in between beds. Gave a deep sigh.——

Session 2

Came willingly but with solemn face. Smiled at sight of dolls, bed, etc. laid out ready.

Stood nurse, doctor, sister in row.

Put Girl 1 in Cot 3.

Boy 2 in Bed 4.

Girl 2 in Bed 1.

Boy 1 in Cot 2.

Baby 1 in Cot 1.

Baby 2 in Bed 3.

Sat in silence looking unhappy. Encouraged by Observer.

Stood mother and father up.

Took father to Cot 2 and mother to Cot 2. Long pause.

T. 'What are they saying?' No response.

Sat looking downcast. Rubbed eyes. Sighed. Observer suggested taking dinner round on trolley.

Took trolley to cot. Long pause.

Further encouragement. Took trolley from cot to centre of ward. Pause. More encouragement. Still looking unhappy and uncomfortable; inquiry led to request to go to toilet. Return. Sat looking unhappy—in silence.

T. 'Now what will they do?'

Pushed trolley and sister fell over—picked up and looked anxiously at Observer.

R. 'She's bended.'

T. 'You see if you can straighten her.'

Straightened sister's legs and stood her by doctor.——

Session 3

Put babies in cots, Boy 2 in Bed 1, Girl 2 in Bed 2, Girl 1 in Bed 3, Boy 1 in Cot 1.

Made all adults stand.

Picked up mother and tried to make her sit on the chair.

She fell off—Ronnie looked at Observer and smiled. Made her stand up.

Made father sit on chair, frowning as he did so. Successful in making father sit, turned to Observer and smiled. Pointed to trolley—top shelf had been stuck in place. Put father on chair, mother standing by Cot 2. Smiled at Observer. Examined doctor, sister and nurse and made them stand. Took father from chair and in straightening his legs rather vigorously pulled his head off. Looked rather alarmed but brightened when Observer produced glue and suggested mending. Stuck head on and put father to bed to get better. Spent a good deal of time trying to make mother sit on chair, showing much patience, then tried to straighten her to make her stand, again very perseveringly.

R. 'Why his hands go up there?' (Doctor's hand was bent up to his shoulder.) Bent nurse and sat her on chair, with success. Turned to Observer and smiled. Took nurse off chair, straightened her and tried to make her stand— propped her against the sister, several times knocking her over and picking her up, looking at Observer from time to time smiling.

Session 4

Refused to come at first so tester said she would come back later and see if he was ready. Came willingly later. Examined chairs and trolley.

Put babies in cots and found that cot sides were movable.

R. 'This can't stand up like that one—can that one go down?' Put all cot sides down.

Put Boy 1 in Cot 1, Girl 2 in Bed 3, Boy 2 in Bed 2. Girl 1 in Bed 1. Stood all adults up.

Bent father and sat him on the chair and smiled at Observer when he fell off. Sat father on chair by Cot 3 and doctor by Cot 2. Doctor fell off and again Ronnie laughed.

R. 'Where's that bed? (Extra bed produced.) His head won't fit in (doctor in bed). See if he can (father). Try mother. Nurse does. Did that broke? (Trolley.)——'

Put baby in Cot 3. Discovered that cot sides came out and spent much time putting them on and off.

R. 'Look, all the cots have sides up. When the babies go in they'll all run away.'

More playing with cot sides. Put baby in cot without side, pushed trolley up against it, pushed all cots together.

R. 'Baby can't get out now.'

Examined father and asked who mended him. Put father in cot.

R. 'He's too big.'

Folded father in half and squashed him in cot and did likewise with sister.

Put baby on trolley. Picked up other baby and examined her.

R. 'She hasn't got any pants on. My baby has pants.'

Put baby in bed with Girl 2. Doctor wheeled baby on trolley to Bed 3.

Doctor doubled up and squashed in cot.

Mother doubled up and put in bed, taken out, straightened and examined.

R. 'Why her coat won't come open?'

Straightened and examined father.

End of session.

Ronnie had a very inhibited approach to the material and appeared quite unhappy at times as he sat in front of it. He came quite willingly each time until the fourth session, when he refused at first but came to play after all the other children had had their turns. He needed a good deal of encouragement and was very anxious about the tester's reaction when he accidentally knocked the dolls over. He was reassured when she smiled and even tried knocking them over deliberately. He began to relax a little at the third session and showed some signs of animation and enjoyment at the fourth session. Only in this last session did he appear to be working out any theme.

Ronnie showed a high percentage of exploratory and organizational play, 22·7 per cent and 43·9 per cent, particularly in the first three sessions. He had comparatively little thematic, 6·1 per cent, and individualized thematic, 12·3 per cent. His aggression was implied rather than active.

As it is more than two years since Ronnie was in hospital it may be that this accounts for his lack of reaction to the material, or, in the light of his history of excessive timidity, it may have been that he did not feel sufficiently secure to work out his tensions. This latter would seem to be borne out by the fact that he played more purposefully at the fourth session.

Norman, aged six years, the youngest of two children from a good home, was hospitalized at the age of four, from May 1959 to July 1960, because of Perthes' disease. For the first five months he was in a hospital where no play provision is made and then transferred to one with an established school. His teacher described him as a bright boy but very spoilt. The treatment for Perthes' disease entails immobilization for a long period, followed by the wearing of a calliper for some time. His teacher reported that Norman became hyper-active for several weeks after his calliper was removed.

Norman played deliberately, unsmilingly, silently, and any attempt to draw him into conversation seemed to inhibit his play, which was by far the most realistic of any of the children. He treated the testing-table as if it were a set for a play and his

146

characters made their exits and entrances either from behind the boards or the floor under the table.

Session 1

Came eagerly, sat down and began to play without introduction. Moved figures purposefully all the time but without speaking.

Put mother and father and children outside the ward. Doctor and nurses inside.

Mother and father came with Boy 1. Doctor went to mother and father. Tried to put Boy 1 on cot—too big—put in bed.

Mother and father talked together. Went from ward. Father fell.

Nurse put to push trolley.

Mother brought father to doctor—showed crack (real) in head—father put to bed—mother went away.

Girl 1 put on floor (real floor). Doctor with trolley put on floor—put Girl 1 on trolley—lifted doctor, trolley and girl to table and wheeled to bed.

Showed concern about father's cracked head and tester promised to mend before next time.

Mother appeared with Boy 1. Doctor fetched Boy 1 and put on trolley. Put mother to bed. Doctor wheeled Boy 1 on trolley to each bed in turn and then put him in cot.

Sister brought to doctor—both went to father in bed.

Sister went to Boy 1 in cot.

Nurse wheeled trolley out of ward—brought in Baby 1. Baby 1 fell off trolley—picked up and put in cot. Nurse wheeled trolley out—brought in Baby 2—fell off trolley—nurse picked up and carried—went to doctor—put baby in cot. Doctor and nurse went out.

Mother went out—brought in Girl 2. Sister went to

147

mother and Girl 2. Sister took Girl 2.

Moved beds around. Examined sister's cap. Put doctor by wall.

Sister took Girl 2. Lifted her above her head and dropped her over her shoulder—picked her up and carried her to bed. Sister went to cot.

Mother went off—fell on floor—doctor and nurse went to mother and brought to ward. Took Boy 1 from bed and put mother in. Doctor took Boy 1 out.

End of session.

All this was carried out with great concentration and complete silence. Tester did not ask questions for fear of disturbing concentration.

Session 2

Picked up all the patients and mother and father and put behind left-hand wall, leaving doctor, sister and nurse in ward. Stood up all dolls behind the wall (hidden from tester). Put nurse and trolley behind right-hand wall. Took sister in one hand and mother in other, placing them facing each other—took doctor to them. Put mother in Bed 1. Took sister to mother.

Examined father. Examined babies—took them to mother in bed, hesitated, put them in doctor's arms and put them in cots. Took Baby 1 from cot—made it creep up behind doctor and push. Father brought Girl 1 to cot. Picked up doctor in mouth. Put doctor and father together. Walked sister and doctor round ward. Took doctor to mother. Mother out of bed. Father brought Boy 2, Girl 2, and Boy 1 on to ward—stood mother behind walls. Took father out to right—then in to mother. Father knocked mother over—put mother in Bed 1, father in Bed 3. Took sister to cots and then to father in bed. Put Girl 2 in Bed 2.

Doctor took Boy 1 and sat him on chair by Cot 3. Doctor went to Boy 2 then round ward, then in bed with mother. Nurse wheeled trolley on to ward to each bed in turn. Doctor and nurse stood together. Sister went to Girl 2 in Bed 3. Put nurse in bed with father. Sister and doctor stood together. Put doctor in bed with Girl 2.

N. 'I've finished now.' (Five minutes early. Only speech volunteered. Did not reply to questions and seemed to be put off by them.)

Session 3

Came quite willingly, after showing the drawing he was doing.

Noticed the extra chair.

N. 'I'm going to put them there.'
Put trolley behind right-hand screen and nurse with it. Stood doctor and sister in middle of ward. Put Boy 1 in Cot 1, Baby 1 in Cot 2, Baby 2 in Cot 3, Girl 2 in Bed 2, Boy 2 in Bed 1.

N. 'I want to put these in bed (mother and father). I want another bed now.'
Put mother and father in bed together. Took mother to Boy 2, sister to nurse, nurse to trolley, wheeled trolley on to ward. Nurse taken to Bed 2 and back to trolley. Locker moved to mother's bed. Trolley to father's bed.

N. 'I haven't got any more of these now' (lockers).
Put trolley between cots.
Stood doctor, sister and nurse together.

N. 'I don't want to play any more now.'
Tester encouraged and discussed with him what might happen.

N. 'This boy (Boy 2) has to have an operation. I'm just pretending he's there now. Mother's having it done now.'

149

Sister taken to each bed in turn. Again said that he didn't wish to continue and returned to his classroom.

Norman showed a high percentage, 54·5 per cent, of tangential behaviour. This was because he withdrew five minutes before the end of the second session, after ten minutes of the third, and flatly refused to come to the fourth. There did not appear to be any specific action leading up to this withdrawal. Subsequent events seemed to indicate that this might have

Doll-play projective tests—average scores

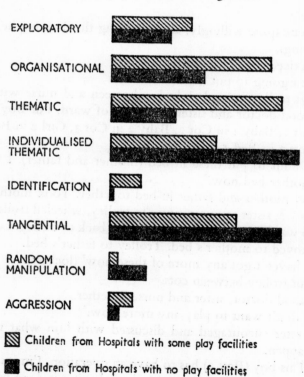

EXPLORATORY

ORGANISATIONAL

THEMATIC

INDIVIDUALISED THEMATIC

IDENTIFICATION

TANGENTIAL

RANDOM MANIPULATION

AGGRESSION

Children from Hospitals with some play facilities

Children from Hospitals with no play facilities

Percentage of actions in each category

Name	Age	Explora-tory	Organi-zational	The-matic	Indivi-dualized The-matic	Identifi-cation	Tan-gential	Tx Random Mani-pulation	Ag-gression −	Ag-gression	Ag-gression +
A Edward	7.0	12.5	15.4	24.0	19.2	1.0	6.7	5.8	1.9	13.5	
A Anne	4.11	17.3	27.2	14.8	4.9	13.6	19.8	1.2		1.2	
A Sarah	6.5	3.8	15.4	46.2	26.9	7.7					
A Ronnie	5.0	22.7	43.9	6.1	12.3		10.6		3.0	1.5	
A Norman	6.0	3.4	13.6	11.4	14.8		54.5			2.3	
Average		11.9	23.1	20.5	15.6	4.5	18.5	1.4	1.0	3.5	—
B David	5.0	16.2	16.2	14.5	32.5	1.7	6.8	4.3	2.6	5.1	
B Joseph	4.6	12.2	15.4	4.9	34.9			9.8	.8	17.9	4.1
B John	4.0	7.2	10.8	13.3	47.0	1.2	1.2	6.0	1.2	10.8	1.2
B Mary	5.0	4.5	9.1	6.8	9.1		68.1	2.3			
B James	5.9	4.5	18.2	6.8	12.5		48.9	3.4	2.3	3.4	
Average		8.9	13.9	9.3	27.2	.6	25.0	5.2	1.4	7.4	1.1

been tied up with his friends' teasing rather than any inhibiting emotion. Much of Norman's individualized thematic play was concerned with putting the adults to bed—sometimes putting two into bed together. He showed 11·4 per cent of thematic play, 14·8 per cent in individualized thematic, and 2·3 per cent of aggression.

Assessment of findings

VARIABLES

From these records there is some very slight indication of differences between the two groups. These cannot be taken as offering any direct proof, since the children studied present far too many variables for a true comparison to be made.

Apart from the more obvious variables of age, length of stay, number of hospitalizations, there are many more which must have influenced the children's play. That the present family situation influenced some of the play is made very obvious in the records of Anne and possibly of Joseph, who both have rather turbulent backgrounds and that a loving happy home produces more thematic play is demonstrated by Sarah. Only with a very few children, by means of the Health Visitor's report, was it possible to find out whether they had been visited frequently while in hospital, and this again would certainly have an influence on their play. The severity of the illness, the care in preparing the child for hospitalization, the attitude of the parents, the quality of the nursing, the time elapsed since the last hospitalization, must all too be in some way reflected.

INDICATION OF DIFFERENCES

The differences indicated are largely in the Thematic, Individualized thematic, Identification and Tangential categories. Children in A group, from hospitals which make some form of play provision, show 20·5 per cent Thematic play as compared to 9·3 per cent in B group, where no play provision is made; 15·6 per cent Individualized thematic as compared to 27·2 per cent; 4·5 per cent Identification as compared to 0·6 per cent; 18·5 per cent Tangential as compared to 25 per cent and 1·4 per cent random manipulation Tx, as compared to 5·2 per cent.

Individualized thematic play is often thought to indicate some degree of disturbance or unresolved anxiety and it is interesting to note that this is 11 per cent higher in the children in B group.

There are 4·0 per cent more examples of Identification among children in A group. Could the inference here be that play and a more permissive atmosphere helped them so to adjust to hospital that they could bear to identify themselves with it? This idea would certainly seem to be supported by the observations on Marie in K, p. 76. It should perhaps be pointed out here that the hospitals making definite play provision are generally more 'child centred' than those making none.

Group B has 6·5 per cent more Tangential, and 3·8 per cent more Tangential X play than Group A. Both these types of play, which show withdrawal from the material, might well indicate some unresolved fear in relation to the hospital situation. The fact that Tangential play often followed after Individualized thematic or Aggressive play seems to support this theory.

Many workers find a high correlation between aggression and insecurity and it may be significant that the children in Group B show a slightly higher score, 5·1 per cent more, of aggression. This seems to support the point of view put for-

ward in the chapter on hospitalization, that the kind of continuous relationship provided by the nursery teacher or nursery nurse helps to give the child a greater feeling of security.

INTERPRETATION

There are many interesting questions of interpretation arising
from these records. Beulah Winstell,[1] discussing doll-play
techniques used in discovering the child's reactions to the
home situation says: 'Totally rejected children exhibit more
overt expression of anti-social and hostile behaviour with less
inhibition and anxiety than those living with their parents and
possibly subjected to ambivalent attitudes.' Is there any tie-up
here with security of home background in relation to hospitalization or alternatively, with security within the hospital
situation? Certainly Sarah's play shows complete lack of aggression whereas Joseph has 22·8 per cent. Or, does aggression
reflect a non-permissive atmosphere and lack of material and
opportunity to work it out at the time. Why do so many
children insist on putting the adults to bed? Is it to gain confidence from mastery of a situation in which formerly they
were the weak victims and the adults were all powerful, or are
they withdrawing from the idea of children being confined to
bed? What is the meaning of Joseph's recurring pattern of
lining up his dolls head to toe after an act of aggression, a
pattern also occurring in Edward's and David's records? Is this
regression to the two-year-old ritual pattern or has it some
psycho-analytic significance? Why does James pile up the
lockers, make the doctor stand on top and push him off? Is he
here expressing aggression arising out of being frustrated by
the doctor's imposition of physical limitation on his activities?
Is the putting of the doctor to bed following this an act of
reparation or a means of reassuring himself that aggression is

[1] Beulah Winstell – (see p. 111).

not wholly destructive? What does David's rather grotesque bending back of the adult males and causing them to fly signify? Do Anne's records show that type of 'scatterbrain' play described by Jackson and Todd[1] as characteristic of unstable children or those in an acute state of anxiety? Is the anxiety, overtly expressed in David's repeated 'You don't have to go back again when you go home', or implicit in much of the individualized thematic play, evidence of unresolved conflicts? Finally, why did Mary, James and Norman withdraw completely from the material after varying lengths of time? Did it evoke memories that were too painful to be met, was it lacking in interest and meaning for them or was their period of hospitalization too long ago for the material to be significant to them?

CONCLUSIONS

These play sessions reveal quite strongly the children's reactions to the hospital situation and a more carefully controlled experiment might well reveal appreciable differences between the two groups. In the light of the experience gained on this pilot scheme it is suggested that children should be selected while in hospital, paired for age, intelligence, home background, frequency of visiting, length of stay and severity of illness. They should then be followed up and tested at a definite period, say six months, after discharge from hospital.

[1] Jackson & Todd, *Child Treatment and the Therapy of Play.*

Conclusions

It would seem from the observations that there is an urgent
need for more attention to play facilities for children in all
hospitals, apart from those few with an established school
including the nursery group. The Ministry of Education, in
their circular on Education of Patients in Hospital, state that
the skilled direction of the young children's play can be ot
special value at a time when they are deprived of a normal
home environment, but not all Education Authorities include
the nursery section in their hospital schools. There would
appear to be no other official provision of play facilities
though individual hospitals do make some arrangements,
with varying degrees of success. It is possible that this problem
will become even more acute when children are treated in
local general hospitals rather than in the larger children's hospitals. The observations certainly show that on the whole the
general hospitals seem to be much less aware of the psychological needs of the children in their wards.

There is a strong indication in the detailed observations that
young children in hospital can derive great benefit from the
right kind of play, given a stable relationship with a skilled
adult and that a plentiful supply of toys is not enough in itself.
The doll-play projective tests would also appear to support
this evidence, though here the investigation was not sufficiently well controlled to offer absolute proof.

The educational and psychological needs of long-stay children have in some measure been recognized, but the short-stay children, whose emotional needs are immediate and equally urgent have very little provision made for them.

Admission to hospital must necessarily increase tension and anxiety in children and they cannot be considered to have received adequate care until they have been provided with satisfactory means of resolving the emotional problems arising from this. It would probably be true to say that no child in hospital is allowed to suffer more physical pain than is absolutely necessary or to be exposed needlessly to danger of infection but it would appear that relatively few children are provided with every possible means of alleviation of mental stress or of the prevention of mental ill-health. Surely 'preventive play therapy' is just as essential as, for example, physiotherapy, which is accepted as an integral part of the Health Service.

Bibliography

General development and play of the pre-school child

Bridges, K., *Social and Emotional Development of the Pre-School Child*. Kegan Paul, 1931.

Buhler, C., *From Birth to Maturity*. Kegan Paul, 1935.

Erikson, E. H., *Childhood and Society*. Imago, 1951.

Gardner, D. E. M., *Education Under Eight*. Longmans Green, 1949.

Gesell, A., *The First Five Years of Life*. Methuen, 1966.

Gesell, A., *Mental Growth of the Pre-School Child*. Macmillan, 1926.

Hartley, Frank and Goldenson, *Understanding Children's Play*. Routledge, 1952.

Isaacs, S., *Intellectual Growth in Young Children*. Routledge, 1935.

Isaacs, S., *Psychological Aspects of Child Development*. Evans, 1937.

Isaacs, S., *The Nursery Years*. Routledge, 1932.

Isaacs, S., *The Educational Value of the Nursery School*. U.L.P., 1954.

Jersild, A. T., *Child Psychology*. Staples, 1960.

de Lissa, L., *Life in the Nursery School*. Longmans, 1949.

Lowenfeld, M., *Play in Childhood*. Gollancz, 1935.

Murphy, L., *Personality in Young Children*. Basic Books, New York, 1957.

Piaget, J., *Play, Dreams and Imitation in Childhood*. Heinemann, 1951.

Sheridan, M. D., *The Development Progress of Infants and Young Children*. H.M.S.O., 1960.

Stern, W., *Psychology of Early Childhood*. Allen and Unwin, 1924.

Stone, J. J. and Church, J., *Childhood and Adolescence*. Random, New York, 1957.

Wall, W. D., *Education and Mental Health*. W.H.O., 1960

Wall, W. D., *The Enrichment of Childhood*. N.S.A., 1960.

Wolff, W., *Personality of the Pre-School Child*. Heinemann, 1947.

Hospitalization

Bowlby, J., *Maternal Care and Mental Health*. W.H.O., 1952.

Bowlby, J., *Separation Anxiety*. Journal of Child Psychology and Psychiatry, Vol. 1, pp. 251–269, 1960

Bowlby, J., *Processes of Mourning*. International Journal of Psycho-Analysis, Vol. XLII, 1961.

Bowlby, J., Ainsworth, Boston and Rosenbluth, *Effects of Mother-Child Separation*. British Journal of Medical Psychology, 1956.

Bowley, A. M., *The Psychological Care of the Child in Hospital*, Livingstone, 1961

Burlingham, D. and Freud, A., *Young Children in Wartime*. 1942.

Cass, J. E., *Play and the Young Child*. Spastic Quarterly, June 1963.

Chesters, G., *The Mothering of Young Children*. Faber and Faber, 1956.

Bibliography

Davidson, E. R., *Play for the Hospitalized Child*. American Journal of Nursing, March 1949.

McPherson, C. A., *Educating Children in Hospital*. Medical World, August 1956.

McPherson, C. A., *The Nursery School in an Orthopaedic Hospital*. New Era, March 1961.

Ministry of Education, *Education of Patients in Hospital*. Circular 312, September 1961.

Moncrieff and Walton, *Visiting Children in Hospital*. British Medical Journal, January 1961.

Plank, E. N., *Working with Children in Hospitals*. Western Reserve University, 1962.

Robertson, J., *Young Children in Hospital*. Tavistock, 1958.

Robertson, J., *Hospitals and Children*. Gollancz, 1962.

Robertson, J., *A Two Year Old Goes to Hospital*. Film.

Robertson, J., *Going to Hospital with Mother*. Film.

W.H.O., *Deprivation of Maternal Care*. W.H.O., 1962.

Winnicott, D. W., *The Child in the Family*. Tavistock, 1957.

Winnicott, D. W., *The Child and the Outside World*. Tavistock, 1957.

Woodward, J. M., *Parental Visiting of Children with Burns*. British Medical Journal, 22nd December 1962.

Play therapy and doll-play

Ammons, *Research and Clinical Applications of the Doll-play Interview*. Journal of Personality, Vol. 21, 1952, pp. 85–90.

Bach, G. R., *Young Children's Play Fantasies*. Psychological Monograph No. 272, 1945.

Erikson, E. H., *Studies in the Interpretation of Play*. Genetic Psychology Monographs 22, 1940, pp. 557–671.

Griffiths, *Imagination in Early Childhood*. Routledge, 1935.

Isaacs, S., *Childhood and After*. Routledge, 1948.

160

Jackson, L. and Todd, K., *Child Treatment and the Therapy of Play*. Methuen, 1948.

N.E.F., *Play and Mental Health*. Monograph No. 3, 1945.

Phillips, R., *Doll Play as a Function of Realism of the Materials and the Length of the Experimental Session*. Journal of Child Development No. 17, 1946.

Pintler, M., *Doll Play as a Function of Experimenter—Child Interaction and Initial Organization of Materials*. Journal of Child Development No. 16, 1945.

Robinson, E. F., *Doll Play as a Function of the Doll Family Constellation*. Journal of Child Development No. 17, 1946.

Rogerson, C. H., *Play Therapy in Childhood*. O.U.P., 1939.

Winstell, B., *The Use of a Controlled Play Situation in Determining Certain Effects of Maternal Attitudes on Children*. Journal of Child Development No. 22, 1951.

L.

Index of Themes

aggression, 18, 28, 64, 94, 100, 104, 110, 111, 120, 121, 124, 130, 133, 141, 142, 152, 153, 154

anxiety, 17, 20, 31, 45, 51, 52, 56, 68, 73, 78, 79, 89, 91, 99, 101, 104, 124, 141, 153, 154, 155, 156

apathy, 37, 40, 45, 47, 58, 71, 86, 92

boredom, 38, 50, 51, 99

chewing, 38, 39, 46, 72, 88, 89

concentration, 29, 45, 64, 75, 76, 80, 83, 84, 85, 88, 89, 92, 94, 99

crying, 20, 24, 37, 39, 40, 44, 46, 53, 54, 55, 80, 87, 88, 91, 109, 124, 127

destruction, 28, 29, 83, 100, 155

doll-play, 28, 36, 43, 44, 55, 56, 57, 61, 62, 81, 82, 84, 85, 99, 100, 106

doll-play projective test, 14, 28, 32, 106, 108, 156

domestic play, 27, 86

dramatic play, 16, 17, 73

head-rolling, rubbing, 41, 42, 45, 46, 50, 51, 52, 55, 56, 57, 67, 70, 73, 74, 76, 78, 87, 92

hospital-play, 28

identification, 110, 137, 141, 153

isolation, 32, 45, 91

language, 30

learning, 30, 31, 89, 100, 101

mental health, 17, 18, 31, 157

'messy' play, 29, 80, 81, 82, 83, 84, 85, 94, 99

mother and child accommo-
dation, 47, 66

nose-picking, 40, 57, 79

painful procedures, 23, 28,
38, 76, 89
painting, 26, 29, 82, 89
playroom, 44, 49, 59, 66, 69,
72, 103

rocking, 56

'safe' toys, 29, 77, 99
security, 21, 22, 25, 26, 29,
90, 109, 154
separation, 13, 19, 20, 21
social contacts, 37, 41, 42, 44,
48, 49, 50, 52, 53, 54, 55,
60, 68, 71, 81, 82, 85, 86,
87, 93, 103

stable adult relationship, 14,
17, 18, 23, 26, 88, 89, 92,
154, 156
sucking, 35, 41, 43, 50, 51, 52,
55, 57, 61, 64, 67, 68, 71,
73, 74

time, 24, 25
touch-hunger, 24, 61, 88

visiting, 21, 33, 35, 37, 39, 42,
44, 47, 49, 52, 55, 57, 60,
62, 66, 69, 72, 75, 77, 83,
86, 118, 152, 155

withdrawn children, 37, 39,
47, 64, 90, 94, 104

yawning and sighing, 40, 45,
50, 57, 60, 67, 73, 74

Index of Persons
mentioned in the text

Bach, G., 106
Bettelheim, B., 24
Bowlby, J., 13, 19, 20, 21, 24, 25
Boyce, E. R., 17
Britton, C., 27
Buhler, C., 24

Church, J., 23

Erikson, E., 15, 28

Frank, L. K., 27

Gesell, A., 18
Goldenson, R. M., 27
Griffiths, R., 106

Hartley, R. E., 27

Isaacs, S., 17–18, 106

Jackson, L., 31, 155

Klein, M., 24

Moncrieff, A., 21

Phillips, R., 107
Piaget, J., 16, 17, 106
Platt Committee Report, 13, 21, 22

Robertson, J., 13, 20, 27
Robinson, E., 106, 108

Spence, J. C., 20

Stern, W., 24
Stone, J., 23
Sylvester, E., 24

Todd, K., 155

Wall, W. D., 17, 18
Walton, A. M., 21
Winnicott, D. W., 20
Winstell, B., 106, 111, 154
Wolff, W., 29
Woodward, J., 21